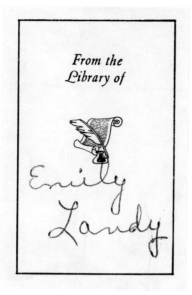

SONGS OF MAN

NORMAN LUBOFF
WIN STRACKE

SONGS OF MAN
THE INTERNATIONAL BOOK OF FOLK SONGS

ILLUSTRATIONS BY
PAUL FREEMAN

BONANZA BOOKS · NEW YORK

COPYRIGHT NOTICE

Country: U. S. & World
Words: P. D. *
Music: N. L.

Rubato

Songs of Man, by Nor-man Lu-boff and Win Stra-cke,

ⓒ Co-py-right Nine-teen six-ty-five by Wal-ton Mu-sic Cor-por-

A tempo (Calypso)

a - tion.

All rights re-served, in - clud — ing the right to re-pro-

duce this book, or an - y por - tions there-of, in an - y

form, ex - cept for the in - clu - sion of brief quo-

ta - tions in a re - view.

Li-brar - y of Con - gress ca - ta - log card num - ber:

Six Five Dash One Four Nine Three Nine.

Printed in the United States of America.

To Dr. Lawrence W. Towner, for making available the facilities of the Newberry Library.

To the Old Town School of Folk Music, for their invaluable assistance, and for making available their facilities.

To Ray Tate, for his advice and assistance in the guitar section.

To Ralph Newman, for his criticism and encouragement.

To Kathryn Baird, Dawn Greening, Kathy Lewis, and Kay Mitchell for their help in the organization of the book.

CONTENTS

INTRODUCTION

The organization of this book stems from the songs themselves. When we were confronted with the task of giving the book form, rather than set up arbitrary divisions into which the songs would be made to conform, we did the reverse. Our method of selecting the songs was based primarily on our love for the songs. Once chosen, surprisingly enough, the songs fell into categories determined by their own similarities. Occasionally, you may be startled to find a song seemingly out of context. Upon examination, you'll find a close relationship with the song or songs which it follows.

Working as we did, we found ample musical support for the old saw, "It's love that makes the world go 'round." We have included more love songs than any other, for that reason. Next in their frequency of occurrence were songs about work and worship—and play (both adult and children). The songs in the remaining categories may appear in folklore less frequently but are certainly of no lesser importance. Bravery, nostalgia, misery—we sing about these too.

"The Cuckoo is a Pretty Bird" and an international bird, indeed. The giving of an entire category to a single bird may seem strange, but this was necessary because of the number of Cuckoo songs which turned up from all over the world. And, how similar in character they are.

We are aware that some of these songs are old favorites and are widely known. Others have been loved and nurtured for generations, but have just begun to travel. Still others were previously known only to specialists. We feel they are all of equal importance, and believe, as they become equally familiar to you, you will agree.

The treatment of folk songs in print has had a long and curious history. In 1765, when Bishop Thomas Percy published his *Reliques,* he ignored the music entirely. In 1883, over a century later, the great American scholar, Francis Child, published his *English and Scottish Ballads* and to all intents and purposes did exactly the same thing. This collection is undoubtedly the best known of its kind and consists of the texts for well over three hundred songs, plus all the variants he could find. As an example, "Lord Rendall" has fifteen English versions included. As an afterthought, he included about fifty tunes in the last volume, without text or accompaniment. They are comparatively useless for any practical purpose.

In 1863, A. P. Berggreen, an inspired Danish folklorist, put together the first truly definitive collection of European folk songs consisting of eleven volumes, covering all the countries of Europe and the British Isles. It included words and music, simply and tastefully arranged for voice and piano. All the texts were printed in their original languages, as well as in Danish translations. Even today, this is a model collection, from the standpoint of the songs included as well as from the respectful way in which they were treated musically.

Unfortunately, toward the end of the nineteenth century, things went awry so far as the publication of folk songs was concerned. The emphasis on the part of most publishers was on single songs or collections designed and arranged to be included in the programs of concert singers. For the most part, in this kind of publication, the simplicity and directness of the songs were obscured by dramatic introductions, elaborate variations, and distracting accompaniments.

With World War II came a revival of interest in folk singing and a distinct protest against the previous kind of "art" song arrangements. As part of that protest, books began to appear with the simplest possible presentations of the songs: the melodic line and text, plus chord symbols for the guitar. This was so effective and direct that most folk music, even today, is printed in this way.

So, the circle is now complete; the songs which sprang from the lips of simple people, which were collected, codified, and evaluated by scholars, and which became the pampered darlings of concert performers are now returning whence they came—the amateurs. These songs are meant to be sung or played by anybody and everybody. Don't permit yourself to be intimidated by the arrangements or performance you hear on radio or records. These songs are not the special prerogative of the professional. In fact, the greatest pleasure is to be derived from singing them yourself.

It isn't necessary to play an instrument. Remember that most of these songs were originally sung without accompaniment. However, if you want accompaniment, it needn't be guitar (or banjo, or dulcimer) in order for you to enjoy folk music. The majority of the songs in this book have simple piano accompaniments as well as guitar symbols. In those cases where we thought it especially appropriate, simple four part vocal arrangements have been made. These can also be played on the piano and/or accompanied by the guitar.

The Arrangements

We chose the keys for the songs with several considerations in mind. All the songs in the book can be sung by anyone with average vocal range and ability. Secondly, we have tried to put the songs in keys which are most compatible to both guitar and piano. The guitar chords are, in all instances, designed to be playable with or without the piano. Occasionally, this makes for a quick succession of chords which may present some difficulties for the guitarist of limited ability. Should this occur, we recommend most strongly that the guitarist omit those chords which create the problems.

The guitar accompaniments should be kept simple, as are the piano accompaniments. At the head of each song is a recommended strum, occasionally more. Every song in this book can be satisfactorily accompanied by the simplest of these strums, tastefully used.

In the section on strums, there are delineated the basic strums, plus a great many more complicated alternatives. Choose any you can play, but remember that the song itself should determine the style of the accompaniment.

By conventional standards, folk music is free and irregular. From verse to verse, the number of syllables and accents can vary enormously. Were one in a position to learn by rote from another singer, this would present no difficulty. The real problem arises when, because of considerations of space, verses must be printed separately from the music. Even in hymns, which tend to be very regular in their metrical patterns, it is difficult enough to make the words conform to the tune. With many folk songs, this is practically impossible.

We have devised a system of printing the additional verses which will do away with these difficulties. The basic time-values are printed across the page with the strong beats underscored. By the simple expedient of placing the words of the additional verses underneath the appropriate beats, it becomes immediately apparent where the stresses of each individual line and word should fall. We've used this system wherever we felt the problem of fitting words to music could occur. In those songs where the only problem is how to start the line, we've used a modification showing only where the first strong beat of each line occurs. Where the additional verses are completely regular and require no explanation, we have simply printed them in the convenient way. It's a simple system, and will, we hope, do away with one of the most vexing problems confronting both the singer and editor.

Early scholars once theorized that folk songs were the product of communal authorship, springing to life as the result of the common experience of a group. Although today it is agreed that most folk songs are the creation of an individual, certain aspects of the former view are true. In the main, folk songs were preserved through the oral tradition, being passed on and handed down verbally. Sometime early in the eighteenth century, Margaret Laidlaw said to Sir Walter Scott: "There was never ane o my songs prentit till ye prentit them yoursel and ye hae spoilt them a'thegither. They were made for singin' and no for readin', but ye hae broken the charm now, and they'll never be sung mair." Obviously, history has proved her wrong. It was not the end, only the beginning. But, however the songs were preserved, each individual or group left its own mark—altering the tunes, adding and deleting lines or verses, sometimes to the point that they bore little resemblance to the original. They may have remained crude or may have become exceedingly subtle. But, one thing has never changed: they are always related to the basic emotions, the strengths and weaknesses born of the experience of mankind. There is, therefore, a universality which communicates instantly, no matter from what period or country the song may come.

We have tried to put songs side by side which document this universality. Sometimes the several songs will spring from the same theme, although each will have its own identity and national character. Often the plot of a song will have such strength that it will occur in different lands with different tunes, but with the story told in almost identical terms. It could have such widely diverse uses as a tragic ballad, a lullaby, a narrative ballad, or a gay, lively song in which the tune belies the tragic quality of the text.

Often a song will stem from some dimly remembered myth or event in man's traditional past, and spring up in startlingly similar versions from widely separated cultures. The frequency with which this occurs shows most clearly the common bond of mankind, transcending national and language barriers, and time and distance—the universality of man demonstrated in the universality of the songs he sings. The feelings of a man for a maid or for his children; the manner in which he laughs at his weaknesses; his admiration for his heroes and his fear and respect for his enemies; his attitude toward his work; his love for his home; these are the things a man sings about; these are his folk songs; these are the *Songs of Man*.

11

ABOUT THE AUTHORS

NORMAN LUBOFF

Norman Luboff's background and experience represent a solid foundation for his distinguished accomplishments. Born in Chicago in 1917, he studied piano and voice as a boy, but it was not until college that he gave any serious thought to making music his profession. After attending the University of Chicago and Central College, however, his decision was made and he enrolled for graduate study in orchestration and composition under the noted composer, Leo Sowerby.

Mr. Luboff's professional career had a three-ply beginning: he taught theory, he began to make commercial arrangements and orchestrations, and—because it was relatively the easiest way to make a start in his chosen field—he employed his trained baritone to fine advantage as a "pops" singer. Soon the young man was appearing regularly on various Chicago radio programs, in local theaters, and on recordings. He gradually became equally sought after as an arranger, for this talent was utilized by many top-ranking radio shows.

Following military service in the Signal Corps during World War II, Mr. Luboff transferred his base of operations to New York. Engaged as a singer at various times by most of the major radio programs, by 1945 the demand for Norman Luboff arrangements had become so great that he gave up singing entirely. Shortly afterward, Hollywood beckoned, and in response to an invitation from Gordon MacRae to join the production staff of "The Railroad Hour," the Luboffs moved to the West Coast. It was only natural that television and motion picture work would follow, and so, for the next seven years Maestro Luboff composed and arranged music for more than 80 moving pictures. In addition, Luboff arrangements have been heard regularly on innumerable important television programs, and still others have been created especially for a star-studded roster of recording artists. He is, however, probably best known for his own recordings which run the complete gamut of musical taste—folk music, Broadway shows, popular songs, and, recently, a classical LP with Leopold Stokowski.

For the past five years the Luboffs and their two children, Peter, nearing 20, and Tina, in her mid-teens, have made their home in London. Summers are generally spent in the south of France, where the head of the house enjoys a variety of sports as well as a connoisseur-sampling of the gastronomic specialties of the region. He finds the Mediterranean atmosphere stimulating to creative impulse, and a short while ago wrote his first show, a fantasy about Robert Burns, entitled *Highland Fling*.

It was not until 1963 that Norman Luboff was able to take sufficient time from his recording activities and his work as an arranger and composer for films and television to embark on his first "in person" tour.

The touring Norman Luboff Choir consists of 30 virtuoso professional singers (accompanied by four gifted and amazingly versatile instrumentalists) whose repertoire is virtually unlimited, and who are equally at home in the cantatas of Bach or the hit tunes of Broadway—all of which they perform with inimitable vitality and superb musicianship. Except for the classical selections, Mr. Luboff has arranged most of the material himself, and he is especially noted, in this day of echo chambers and other "hoked up" electronic devices, for the clarity and naturalness of his arrangements, and for an eminently singable style.

Now, yet another facet of Mr. Luboff's varied talents manifests itself. A devotee and avid collector of the folk music of all peoples since the days of his first musical awareness, the Maestro presents in these pages an opus which has been, literally, all of his adult life in preparation. Not a few of these songs will already be familiar to owners of his recordings. Many of them were discovered in recent years, during which the nature of his work and fortunes have permitted extended periods of travel and residence abroad. All 184 of them are here set forth by the man who—perhaps better than anyone else now living—knows and understands the human voice, the human heart, and the human fellowship they make possible.

WIN STRACKE

Win Stracke enjoys the cherished distinction of being known as "Chicago's minstrel," though he has acquired a national reputation through his network TV and radio shows and his recordings.

His intimate identification with Chicago began at the age of one, when his father, a clergyman, moved to the city from Kansas. With the exception of three years' duty in Europe during World War II, Win has spent his life living and singing in Chicago. He attended Senn High School, and participated in the choral group there directed by Noble Cain. Encouraged to study voice, he became soloist in many of Chicago's leading Protestant and Catholic churches, and has performed cantorial duties in several temples.

He became a radio performer at WLS in 1931, and appeared on such well-remembered network and local programs as "Hymns of all Churches," "Theater of the Air," "Alec Templeton Time," "National Barn Dance," "The Garroway Show," and Northwestern University's documentary, "The Meaning of America." During those years he began his long association as an active member of the musicians' union.

In 1948, because of his growing interest in folk music, Win and Studs Terkel organized the first "I Come for to Sing" programs, which became models for similar public performances all over the country. Several of the performers went on to become nationally recognized singers and authorities on folk music. During the famed "Chicago School" period of network TV (1950-1955), Win was the most widely used performer in the city, appearing as co-star on such network shows as the prize-winning "Studs' Place," "Hawkins Falls," "Magic Slate," and his own celebrated children's show, "Animal Playtime."

With the exodus of network TV from Chicago, Win concentrated on recordings and personal appearances, with occasional local TV appearances. In 1963 he co-starred with the George Latshaw puppets in NBC-TV's first "Children's Theater" special, as the fearful giant in James Thurber's "Quillow and the Giant." He has appeared many times over the years in classical concerts, and as soloist with the Chicago, Grant Park, and Women's Symphony Orchestras.

His active interest in the life and times of the people around him found expression in a number of his own compositions. One of the more famous politically oriented songs is "The Ballad of the 43rd Ward," written in honor of the local alderman and the colorful history of one of Chicago's most cosmopolitan wards. He also wrote and recorded many of the songs he presented on the "Animal Playtime" show.

In 1957 Win founded The Old Town School of Folk Music. Originating in a living room guitar class, under his direction the School has grown from a place to learn simple song accompaniments to an organization that offers important contacts with many kinds of traditional music and performers, and an opportunity for people with a natural affinity for music to develop their singing and playing abilities for their own pleasure.

Win's personal interest in Abraham Lincoln and the Civil War has led to membership in The Civil War Round Table. He has been a regularly featured performer at the Lincoln's Birthday dinners held annually in Springfield, Illinois, and this year was a member of a delegation invited by President Lyndon B. Johnson to a special Lincoln's Birthday luncheon at the White House.

One of the many programs he has prepared in connection with the life of Abraham Lincoln was "Songs Lincoln Loved," which he presented with faculty members of The Old Town School of Folk Music during "Illinois Day" celebrations at the New York World's Fair in 1964.

He is presently working on a book about Old Town, the heart of the 43rd ward and his home neighborhood for many years. The Old Town School of Folk Music is located there, and many of its residents are, like Win Stracke, active in the artistic and cultural life of the Midwest.

In spite of this impressive list of credits, Win's greatest performing pleasure is to take guitar in hand, dig into his bulging song bag, and share with his listeners the singing of these wonderful songs which reflect the lives and aspirations of people everywhere.

ABOUT THE ARTIST

PAUL FREEMAN

To some people, Paul Freeman is a modern embodiment of the Renaissance Artist—constantly probing, seeking new forms of expression, experimenting in new media, and unafraid of facing a true challenge to his imagination and abilities. The "easy way" or the "conventional way" are not for him. When he began sculpting, he chose the "lost wax method" which many of his contemporaries find too difficult to attempt. Dissatisfied with new plastic paints, he devised his own acrylic formula.

Freeman's concentration upon his art is as intense as his output is prolific. His workday often lasts 72 hours without a break; and after a few hours sleep, he returns to continue his explorations into form, line, and color. Thus, in the past 10 years, his canvases number over 2,000, and his works in other media exceed even that number. Within this framework, he has also found time to make films for television, to design stage sets, and to write the humorous book, "An Introduction to Sigmund Freud, M.D., and Psychoanalysis, published earlier this year by Prentice-Hall.

His paintings and sculpture have been unabashedly concerned with human feelings and experiences. He captures the awkward grace of isolated children, the leap of the soaring dancer. The despair of the defeated soldier is overwhelming in his bronze series, Armageddon, and in his Don Quixote lies the bitter humor and agony of the undaunted and restless searcher. His work has been exhibited in museums throughout the world, from the Museum of Modern Art in New York to the Tel Aviv Museum in Israel. Since 1956 he has had seven one-man shows in New York as well as several shows in cities across the country.

Long before the folk song became fashionable and popular, his studio was filled with the music of balladiers, street singers, minstrels, and the chain gang. This long-time love of the songs of man can be seen in his illustrations for this book. They glow with wit, tenderness, power, despair, loneliness, toil, and love. In approaching this monumental project, Paul Freeman researched the unfamiliar songs thoroughly—often conferring with Norman Luboff who played and sang them for him. The result is that each illustration carries through the concept of each song in this collection.

Born in New York City, Freeman left when he was in his early twenties to travel and live in the western United States.

Today, when they are not traveling throughout Europe, the Middle East, or the Orient, Paul Freeman and his wife, a practicing psychoanalyst, live in New York.

MEN AND WOMEN
AT WORK

CALLER HERRIN'

A street cry extended to a full length song. It's changed considerably from the original art song by Baroness Nairne and Nathaniel Gow in the late eighteenth century.

SCOTLAND

Words by Baroness Nairne
Tune by Nathaniel Gow
Arr. by N. L.

STRUM: Va

Freely not too fast ($\quarternote$ = 72)

Refrain

Buy my cal-ler her-rin. They're bon-nie fish and hale-some far-in'.

Buy my cal-ler her-rin'. Just new-drawn frae the Forth. *Fine*

Verse

When ye were sleep-in' on your pil-lows, dream'd ye aught of our poor fel-lows,

Dark-lin' as they faced the bil-lows, all to fill our wo-ven wil-lows? *D.C. al Fine*

18

Refrain: Buy my caller herrin'. They're bonnie fish and halesome farin'.
Buy my caller herrin'. Just new drawn frae the Forth.

2. And when the creel of herrin' passes, ladies clad in silk and laces
Gather in their braw pelisses, cast their heads and screw their faces.
Refrain:

3. Now neighbors, wives, attend my tellin'. When the bonnie fish you're sellin',
At your word e'er be your dealin'. Truth will stand when all seems failin'.
Last Refrain: Buy my caller herrin'. Oh, ye may call them vulgar farin';
Wives and mithers most despairin' call them lives of men.

CLEAR THE TRACK

This shanty is a variation of the Irish song "Shula Agra." A capstan shanty for short pulls, but probably used for loading as well.

STRUM: IVA or IA

BRITISH ISLES
and
NORTH AMERICA
Arr. by N.L.

Moderately fast, in strict rhythm (♩=92)

Verse

O, the smart-est clip-per you can find, Ah-

hee, ah-ho, are you most done? Is the Marg-'ret Ev-ans of the

Black X___ Line, So clear a-way the track, let the bull-gine run.

Refrain

To my hey rig-a-jig in a low back car, Ah-hee, ah-ho, are

Em / **Em** / **Am**

you most done? With Li - za Lee all on my__ knee, So

Em / **Bm(7)** / **Em** / **Em** / **Em**

clear a - way the track, let the bull-gine run.

2. O, the times are hard and the wages low.
Ah-hee, ah-ho, are you most done?
O, it can't get worse, so we're bound to go,
So clear away the track, let the bullgine run.
Refrain

3. O, the winds were foul and the work was hard,
Ah-hee, ah-ho, are you most done?
From the Liverpool docks to the Brooklyn yard.
So clear away the track, let the bullgine run.
Refrain

THE CRUISE OF THE BIGALER

A fresh-water forecastle shanty. The *Bigaler* was notorious as one of the slowest ships on the Great Lakes.

STRUM: IA

UNITED STATES

Arr. by N. L.

Lively ($\quad$=100)

Verse

Come all you boys and lis-ten; a song I'll sing to you. It's all a-bout the Big-a-ler, and of her jol-ly crew. In Mil-wau-kee last Oc-to-ber I chanc'd to get a site In the schoon-er call'd the Big-a-ler, be-long-ing to *De-trite.

Refrain

Watch her, catch her, jump up in her ju-ber-ju.

22

* Detroit

Give her sheet and let her go; we're the lads can pull her thru. Oh,
don't you hear the howl-ing of the winds a-blow-ing free, On our
down trip to Buf-fa-lo from Mil - wau - kee.

2. 'Twas on one Sunday morning just at the hour of ten,
   When the *Nickle Roberts* towed us into Lake Michigan.
   Oh, there we made our canvas in the middle of the fleet.
   Oh, the wind hauled to the southard and we had to give her sheet.
   Refrain:

3. The wind come from the south-southeast, it blowed both stiff and strong!
   You had orter seen the *Bigaler* as she plowed Lake Michigan.
   Oh, far beyond her foaming bows the fiery waves to fling,
   With ev'ry stitch of canvas and her course was wing and wing.
   Refrain:

4. We made Skilagalee and Wabbleshanks, the entrance to the straits,
   And might have passed the whole fleet there if they'd hove to and wait;
   But we drove them all before us the nicest you ever saw
   Clear out into Lake Huron thru the Straits of Mackinaw.
   Refrain:

5. We made the light and kept in sight of Michigan's east shore,
   A–booming for the river as we'd often done before.
   And when abreast Port Huron Light, our anchor we let go;
   The tug *Kate Moffet* came and took the *Bigaler* in tow.
   Refrain:

6. Thru Lake St. Clair they towed us till we got to the river light,
   Lake Erie for to wander, her blust'ring winds to fight.
   Then the wind blew from the sou'west and our hearts began to glow
   With the thought of all the good things waiting there in Buffalo.
   Refrain:

23

THE HOUSEWIFE'S LAMENT

Written in the style of the Irish topical ballad, it is
known also as "Life Is A Toil" and "Housekeeper's Lament."

UNITED STATES

STRUM: I-B

Arr. by N. L.

Moderately fast (♩=160)

Verse

One day I was walk-ing, I heard a com-plain-ing, And
saw an old wom-an, the pic-ture of gloom. She
gazed at the mud on her door-step ('twas rain-ing) And
this was her song as she wield-ed her broom:

Refrain

"Oh, life is a toil,___ and love is a trou-ble,___

24

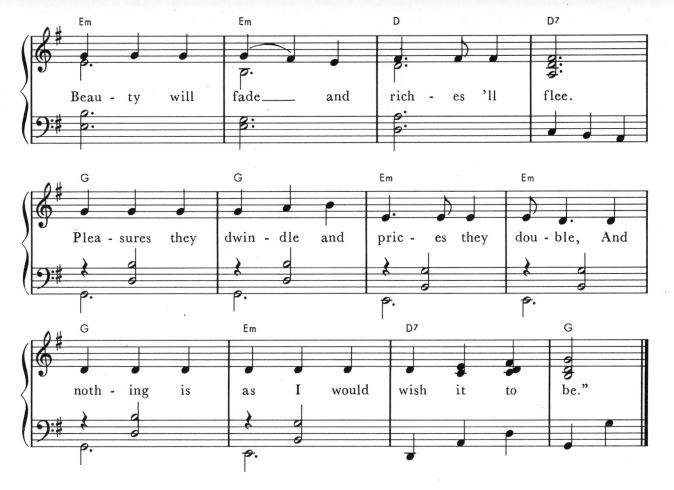

Beau - ty will fade___ and rich - es 'll flee.

Plea - sures they dwin - dle and pric - es they dou - ble, And

noth - ing is as I would wish it to be."

2. "There's too much of worriment goes to a bonnet,
There's too much of ironing goes to a shirt.
There's nothing that pays for the time you waste on it;
There's nothing that lasts us but trouble and dirt."
Refrain

3. "In March it is mud, it is slush in December;
The midsummer breezes are loaded with dust.
In fall the leaves litter. In muddy September
The wallpaper rots and the candlesticks rust."
Refrain

4. "There are worms on the cherries and slugs on the roses,
And ants in the sugar and mice in the pies.
The rubbish of spiders no mortal supposes;
And ravaging roaches and damaging flies."
Refrain

5. "It's sweeping at six and it's dusting at seven.
It's victuals at eight and it's dishes at nine.
It's potting and panning from ten to eleven;
We scarce break our fast till we plan how to dine."
Refrain

6. "With grease and with grime, from corner to center,
Forever at war and forever alert.
No rest for a day lest the enemy enter;
I spend my whole life in struggle with dirt."
Refrain

7. "Last night in my dreams I was stationed forever"
On a far little rock in the midst of the sea.
My one chance of life was a ceaseless endeavor
To sweep off the waves as they swept over me."
Refrain

8. "Alas! 'Twas no dream; ahead I behold it.
I see I am helpless my fate to avert."
She lay down her broom, her apron she folded,
She lay down and died and was buried in dirt.
Refrain

25

BUFFALO SKINNERS

A narrative ballad, known also as "Crego," this is a song complaining of deceit and danger in which the grievance committee uses rather desperate measures!

STRUM: IVc or Ic

UNITED STATES

Moderately (♩. = 110)

'Twas in the town of Jacks - bo - ro in the spring of sev - en - ty three, A man by the name of Cre - go came step - ping up to me, say - ing: "How d'ya do, young fel - low, how would you like to go And spend a sum - mer pleas - ant - ly on the range of the buf - fa - lo?"

26

2. "Yes,   I will pay good wages,
  Give   transportation, too,
  Pro–   vided you will go with me
  And   stay the summer thru;
  But   if you should grow homesick,
  Come   back to Jacksboro,
  I   won't pay transportation from
  The   range of the buffalo."

3. It's   now our outfit was complete,
  Seven   able bodied men,
  With   navy six and needle gun,
  Our   troubles did begin.
  Our   way it was a pleasant one,
  The   route we had to go,
  Un–   til we cross'd Pease River,
  On the   range of the buffalo.

4. It's   now we've cross'd Pease River,
  Our   troubles have begun.
  The   first damn tail I went to rip,
  Christ!   How I cut my thumb!
  While   skinning the damned old stinkers,
  Our   lives they had no show,
  For the   Indians watch'd to pick us off
  While   skinning the buffalo.

5. He   fed us on such sorry chuck
  I   wished myself 'most dead;
  It was   old jerk'd beef, croton coffee,
     And sour bread.
  Pease   River's as salty as hellfire.
  The   water I never could go.
  Oh,   God! I wish'd I had never come
  To the   range of the buffalo.

6. Our   hearts were cased with buffalo hocks,
  Our   souls were cased in steel,
  And the   hardships of that summer
  Would   nearly make us reel.
  While   skinning the damned old stinkers,
  Our   lives they had no show,
  For the   Indians watched to pick us off
  On the   hills of Mexico.

7. The   season being near over,
  Old   Crego, he did say
  The   crowd had been extravagant,
  Was in   debt to him that day.
  We   coaxed him and we begg'd him,
  And   still it was no go.
  We   left old Crego's bones to bleach
  On the   range of the buffalo!

8. Oh, it's   now we've cross'd Pease River,
  And   homeward we are bound.
  No   more in that hellfired country
  Shall   ever we be found.
  Go   back to our wives and sweethearts,
  Tell   others not to go,
  For   God's forsaken the buffalo range,
  And the   damned old buffalo.

NEW OYSTERS

Street cries were often made into songs. This was made into a Round.

Moderately (♩ = 100)

ENGLAND

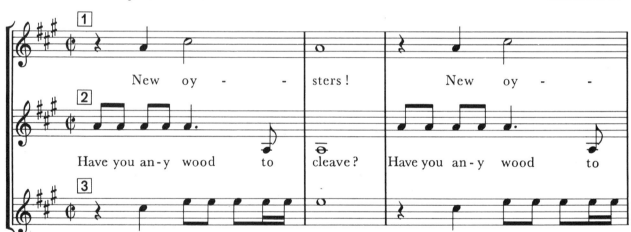

1 New oy - - sters! New oy - -

2 Have you an-y wood to cleave? Have you an-y wood to

3 What kitch-en stuff have you, maids? What kitch-en stuff have you,

28

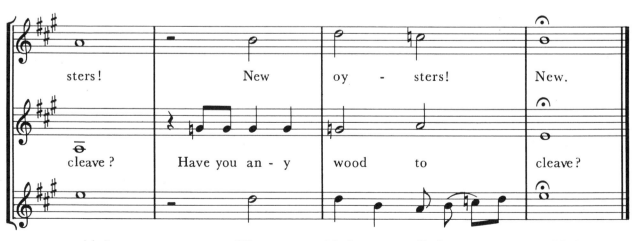

sters! New oy - sters! New.

cleave? Have you an - y wood to cleave?

maids? What kitch - en stuff have you, maids?

CHAIRS TO MEND

Attributed to William Hayes, 1706-1777, it is another round formed from street cries.

UNITED STATES

Moderately fast (♩ = 112)

1 Chairs to mend, old chairs to mend, Rush or cane bot-tom, old

chairs to mend, old chairs to mend. New **2** mack-er-el, new

mack-er-el. New mack-er-el, new

mack-er-el. **3** Old rags, an-y old rags, Take

mon-ey for your old rags, an-y hare-skins or rab-bit skins.

29

GREENLAND WHALE FISHERY

This came from the British whalers, but was widely known and sung by the Americans as well.

BRITISH ISLES
UNITED STATES

STRUM: IXA or IA

Arr. by N. L.

Marcato (♩ = 112)

'Twas in eigh - teen hun - dred and fif - ty three, And of

June the thir - teenth__ day, That our gal - lant ship her__

30

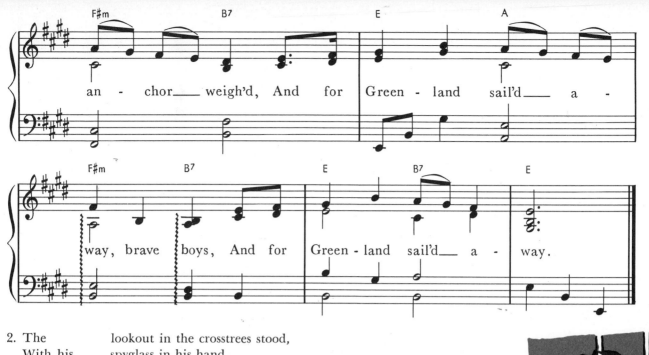

an - chor___ weigh'd, And for Green - land sail'd___ a -

way, brave boys, And for Green - land sail'd___ a - way.

2. The   lookout in the crosstrees stood,
   With his   spyglass in his hand.
   "There's a   whale, there's a whale, there's a whalefish," he cried,
   "And she   blows at every span, brave boys,
   And she   blows at every span."

3. The   captain stood on the quarterdeck,
   And a   fine little man was he.
   "Over-   haul! Overhaul! Let your davit-tackles fall,
   And   launch your boats for sea, brave boys,
   And   launch your boats for sea."

4. Now the   boats were launched and the men aboard,
   And the   whale was in full view;
   Re-   solv-éd was each seaman bold
   To   steer where the whalefish blew, brave boys,
   To   steer where the whalefish blew.

5. We   struck that whale, the line paid out,
   But she   gave a flourish with her tail;
   The   boat capsized and four men were drowned,
   And we   never caught that whale, brave boys,
   And we   never caught that whale.

6. "To   lose the boat," our captain said,
   "It   grieves my heart full sore;
   But,   oh, to lose four gallant men,
   It   grieves me ten times more, brave boys,
   It   grieves me ten times more."

7. "The   winter star doth now appear,
   So,   boys, we'll anchor weigh;
   It's   time to leave this cold country,
   And   homeward bear away, brave boys,
   And   homeward bear away."

8. O,   Greenland is a dreadful place,
   A   land that's never green,
   Where there's   ice and snow, and the whalefishes blow,
   And the   daylight's seldom seen, brave boys,
   And the   daylight's seldom seen.

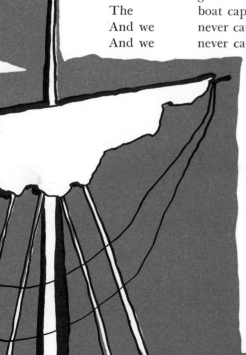

DASHING AWAY WITH THE SMOOTHING IRON

Known also as "Driving Away, etc.,"
it's a gay rollicking tune.

STRUM: IVc or Ic

ENGLAND

Arr. by N. L.

'Twas on a Mon - day morn - ing When I be - held my

dar - ling. oh, she was fair and charm - in' In ev' - ry high de -

gree. Yes, she was neat and will - ing, oh, A - pick - ing up her

32

lin - en clothes. Dash-ing a - way with the smooth-ing iron,

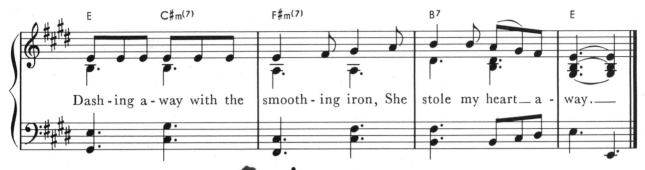

Dash-ing a - way with the smooth-ing iron, She stole my heart a - way.

2. 'Twas on a Tuesday morning
   When I beheld my darling;
   O, she was fair and charmin'
   In every high degree.
   Yes, she was neat and willing, O,
   A-soaping of her linen clothes.
   Dashing away, with the smoothing iron, (twice)
   She stole my heart away.

3. 'Twas on a Wednesday morning,
   When I beheld my darling;
   ·O, she was fair and charmin'
   In every high degree.
   Yes, she was neat and willing, O,
   A-starching of her linen clothes,
   Dashing away, etc.

4. 'Twas on a Thursday morning,
   When I beheld my darling;
   O, she was fair and charmin'
   In every high degree.
   Yes, she was neat and willing, O,
   A-hanging out her linen clothes,
   Dashing away, etc.

5. 'Twas on a Friday morning,
   When I beheld my darling;
   O, she was fair and charmin'
   In every high degree.
   Yes, she was neat and willing, O,
   A-rolling down her linen clothes,
   Dashing away, etc.

6. 'Twas on a Saturday morning,
   When I beheld my darling;
   O, she was fair and charmin'
   In every high degree.
   Yes, she was neat and willing, O,
   Ironing of her linen clothes,
   Dashing away, etc.

7. 'Twas on a Sunday morning,
   When I beheld my darling;
   O, she was fair and charmin'
   In every high degree.
   Yes, she was neat and willing, O,
   A-wearing of her linen clothes,
   Dashing away, etc.

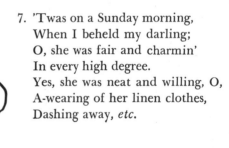

33

DOWN IN A COAL MINE

This is a good example of a common paradox to be found in folk songs: a bitter text set to a happy tune.

STRUM: I-A or IX-A

ENGLAND

Arr. by N. L.

Moderately (♩=116)

Verse

I am a jov - ial col - li - er, as jov - ial as can be, but —

if the trade is ver - y bad, it means a lot to me. And

if I stum - ble with my tongue, I've one ex - cuse to say: It's —

not the col - lier's heart that's wrong, it's the head that goes a - stray.

Refrain

Down — in a coal mine un - der - neath the ground,

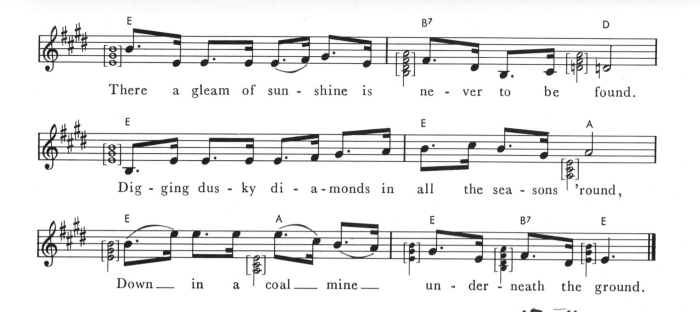

There a gleam of sun - shine is ne - ver to be found.

Dig - ging dus - ky di - a - monds in all the sea - sons 'round,

Down in a coal mine un - der - neath the ground.

2. How bravely all them collier lads, they toil beneath the ground,
Digging for the coal as do the days and nights go round;
And anxiously their fam'lies wait—how often it is said,
You never know by nightfall just how many might be dead.
Refrain

3. How little do the rich men care, who sit at home secure,
What dangers all the colliers dare, and hardships they endure.
The very fires they light at home to cheer them and their wives
Perhaps were kindled at the cost of jovial colliers' lives.
Refrain

4. Then cheer up, lads, and make the most of ev'ry joy you can,
And always let your mouth be such that best does suit a man.
For let the times be good or bad, we'll yet be jovial souls,
And what would Britain be without the lads that dig for coals?
Refrain

MILKING CROON I

Milking can evidently be done in odd meters. The original edition
gave the instruction "Tenderly enticing, but strictly rhythmical."

STRUM: IX

SCOTLAND
Eng. Version by W. S.
Arr. by N. L.

Slowly (♩=88)

Rope of   silk for my own dear brown cow, Rope of hemp for the town's black cat - tle. Cow-herd
Il   a   bho-lag-ain il bho-m'agh-an, il a bho-lag-ain il___ bho m'agh-an, Il a
** *Eel a   vo-lak-in eel vo ma-an, eel a vo-lak-in eel___ vo ma-an, Eel a*

Pat - rick and milk - maid Bri - die, God___ save   you and shield___ you___ ev - er.
bho   lag-ain il bho-m'agh-an Mo-chrodh___ laoigh air gach taobh___ an___ aoh-ainn.
vo   lak-in eel vo ma-an, Mo-chro'___ lur   air gach turv___ an___ av-an.

2. O, let down thy warm milk, my brown one,
For my love is a-waiting for me.
O, his song's like the dove's sweet cooing,
God save him and shield him forever.

2. Bo lurach, bo na hairidh,
Bo a' bhatheach mathair laogh,
Buachaille Padruig is van'chaig Bride
D'ar sion d'ar dion 's d'ar comhnadh.

Suggested accompaniment : An open fifth, G and D on the first beat
of each measure.

** Phonetic pronunciation of Scottish text.

36

MILKING CROON II

STRUM: G

This has a real lilt with its capricious syncopations.
The tempo is to be set by the
speed with which one can milk.

SCOTLAND

Eng. version by W. S.
Arr. by N. L.

Moderately (♩=144)

Ho   hee -   - o   vo,   hee -   o   vo. _____
Ho   hee -   - o   vo,   hee -   o   vo. _____

Shane   my_____   loved   one's   wait -   ing   for   me.
Seel   do_____   vane - uh   vo _____   goon. _____

Ho   hee - o   vo,   hee -   -   -   o   vo. _____
Ho   hee - o   vo,   hee -   -   -   o   vo. _____

Told   me   last   night_____   he   did   a - dore   me.
Shane   's   a'   gee - oos' - aich,   hee -   o   vo, _____

Refrain

Ho - hee - o _____   vo,   hee -   o   vo, _____
Ho - hee - o _____   vo,   hee -   o   vo, _____

When   we're _____   fin - ished   I'll   go   to   him
Seel   do, _____   van - uh   vo _____   goon. _____

Ho   hee -   - o   vo,   hee -   o   vo. _____
Ho   hee -   - o   vo,   hee -   o   vo. _____

Let   it   down   quick - ly,   or   I'll - lose   him.
Shane   sahn   ee - on   drane   hee -   o   vo. _____

37

THE FARMER IS THE MAN

The lot of the farmer has never been easy. Drought, death, and taxes; overproduction, underproduction; but "the farmer is the man who feeds them all."

STRUM: I-A   UNITED STATES

Moderately (♩ = 120)   Arr. by N. L.

Verse

When the farm-er comes to town, with his wag-on bro-ken down, Oh, the

far-mer is the man who feeds them all! If you'll on-ly look and see, I'm

sure you will a-gree That the farm-er is the man who feeds them all!

Refrain

The farm-er is the man, the farm-er is the man,

Lives on cre-dit 'till the fall; Then they take him by the hand, and they

lead him from the land, And the mer-chant is the man who gets it all.

2. O, the lawyer hangs around while the butcher cuts a pound,
But the farmer is the man who feeds them all!
O, the preacher and the cook go a-strolling by the brook,
And the farmer is the man who feeds them all!
Refrain

3. When the butcher says he's broke, and the merchant's up in smoke,
They forget that it's the farmer feeds them all!
It would put them to the test if the farmer took a rest;
Then they'd know that it's the farmer feeds them all.
Refrain

Last Refrain
The farmer is the man, the farmer is the man,
Lives on credit 'till the fall—
With the int'rest rate so high, it's a wonder he don't die,
For the mortgage man's the one who gets it all.

39

THE WARK OF THE WEAVERS

Note the similarity to "The Farmer is the Man." The quality of this song comes out best when it is sung in the dialect.

STRUM: I-A

SCOTLAND

Arr. by N. L.

Lively, but not too fast (♩ = 132)

Verse

We're a' met the-gi-ther here to sit and to crack, Wi' oor glass-es in oor hands and oor wark up-on oor back; And there's no trade a-mang them a' can ei-ther mend or mak', If it was-na for the wark o' the weav-ers.

Refrain

If it was-na for the weav-ers, what would they do? We

40

would-na ha'e claith made o' oor woo'? We would-na ha'e a coat, nei-ther

black nor blue, If it was-na for the wark o' the weav-ers.

2. The hireman chirls, they mock us and crack aye aboot's.
They say that we are thin-faced, bleach'd like cloots;
But yet for a' their mockery, they canna' do wi' oot's.
Na! They canna want* the wark o' the weavers.
Refrain:

3. There's oor wrichts and oor slaters and glaziers and a',
Oor doctors and oor ministers, and them that live by law,
And oor friends in South Amerikay, tho' them we never saw,
But we ken they wear the wark o' the weavers.
Refrain:

4. There's oor sailors and oor soldiers; we ken they're a' bauld,
But if they had na cla'es, faith, they couldna fecht for cauld.
The high, the low, the rich, and puir a'body young and auld,
They wi'nna want the wark o' the weavers.
Refrain:

5. There's folk that's independent o' ither tradesmen's wark,
The women need nae barber, and dykers need nae clark;
But none o' them can do wi'oot a coat or a sark.
Na! They canna want the wark o' the weavers.
Refrain:

6. The weaving is a trade that never can fail,
As lang's we need ae cloot to keep another hale;
So let us aye be merry ower a bicker o' guid ale,
And drink tae the health o' the weavers.
Refrain:

*want: to be without

CLICK GO THE SHEARS

A rousing sheep-shearing song, it includes many technical instructions for those contemplating a similar career.

STRUM: IA

AUSTRALIA

Arr. by N. L.

Moderately (♩=116)

Verse

Twen-ty thou-sand a-cres sounds like a lot. It

ain't when you're graz-in' all the sheep we've got. There's plen-ty o' food and wa-ter, so

they nev-er kick. They're hap-py till they hear the shears go click, click, click.

Refrain

Click go the shears, boys, click, click, click. Wide is the blow and his

hands are mov-ing quick. Oh, you pull out a sheep and he

lands you a kick, and still you hear the shears a-go-ing click, click, click.

42

2. You take off the belly wool and finickle out the crutch,
Then go up the neck, for the rules they are such.
You clean 'round the horns and the first shoulder down,
A long blow up the back and then you turn around.
Refrain

3. And when the shearing's over and we've all got our check,
We'll roll up our blueys and we're off on the track.
The first town we come to, well, there we'll have a spree,
And ev'ry one that comes along 'll join in with me.
Refrain

ONE MORE DAY

A "homeward bound" capstan shanty. Said to be of Negro origin.

STRUM: IA

UNITED STATES

Arr. by N. L.

Moderately (♩=104)

Verse

Oh, have you heard the news, my John-ny? One more ____ day. We're
Oh, heave and sight the anch-or, John-ny. One more ____ day. Oh,

home — ward bound to — mor — row, One more ____ day. On — ly
heave and sight the anch — or. One more ____ day. On — ly

Refrain

one more ___ day, my John-ny, One more ____ day. Oh,

rock and row me o — ver, One more ____ day.

43

RED IRON ORE

A Great Lakes come-all-ye, this text is sung to many different tunes. This version is of Irish origin.

STRUM: IB

UNITED STATES

Arr. by N. L.

Moderately fast ($\downarrow = 120$)

Verse

Come all you bold sail-ors that fol-low the lakes, On an i-ron ore ves-sel your liv-ing to make. I shipp'd in Chi-ca-go, bid a-dieu to the shore, Bound a-way to Es-ca-na-ba for red i-ron ore.

Refrain
a tempo

Der-ry down, down, down, der-ry down.

2. In the month of September, the seventeenth day,
Two dollars and a quarter is all they would pay;
And on Monday morning, the *Bridgeport* did take
The *E. C. Roberts* out into the lake.
Refrain:

3. The wind from the south'ard sprang up a fresh breeze,
And away through Lake Michigan the *Roberts* did sneeze.
Down through Lake Michigan the *Roberts* did roar,
And on Friday morning we passed through death's door.
Refrain:

4. This packet, she howled 'cross the mouth of Green Bay,
And before her cutwater, she dashed the white spray.
We rounded the sandpoint, our anchor let go;
We furled in our canvas and the watch went below.
Refrain:

5. Next morning we hove alongside the *Exile*,
And soon was made fast to an iron ore pile.
They lowered their chutes, and like thunder did roar;
They spouted into us that red iron ore.
Refrain:

6. Some sailors took shovels, while others got spades,
And some took wheelbarrows, each man to his trade.
We looked like red devils, our fingers got sore;
We cursed Escanaba and that damned iron ore.
Refrain:

7. The tug *Escanaba*, she towed out the *Minch;*
The *Roberts* she thought she had left in a pinch,
And as she passed by us, she bid us goodbye,
"We'll meet you in Cleveland next Fourth of July!"
Refrain:

8. Through Louse Island it blew a fresh breeze;
Made the Foxes, the Beavers, the Skillageles.
We flew by the *Minch* for to show her the way,
And she ne'er hove in sight till we were off Thunder Bay.
Refrain:

9. Across Saginaw Bay the *Roberts* did ride
With the dark and deep water rolling over her side,
And now for Port Huron the *Roberts* must go,
Where the tug *Kate Williams*, took us in tow.
Refrain:

10. We went thru North Passage. Oh, Lord, how it blew!
And all 'round the Dummy, a large fleet there came, too.
The night being dark, Old Nick it would scare;
We hove up next morning, and for Cleveland did steer.
Refrain:

11. Now the *Roberts* is in Cleveland, made fast, stem and stern,
And over the bottle we'll spin a big yarn.
But Captain Harvey Shannon had ought to stand treat
For getting into Cleveland ahead of the fleet.
Refrain:

CHICAGO
Lake
Michigan
Green Bay
Cleveland
Louse
ISLAND
foxes
Beavers
Skillageles
THUNDER
BAY
Saginaw Bay
Port Huron
north passage
the Dummy

THE BOSTON COME-ALL-YE

A forecastle shanty, and a
favorite with the fishermen of the Newfoundland Banks. The tune is a variant of "Blow the Wind Southerly."

STRUM: IIB

UNITED STATES

Moderately fast (♩=136)

Arr. by N. L.

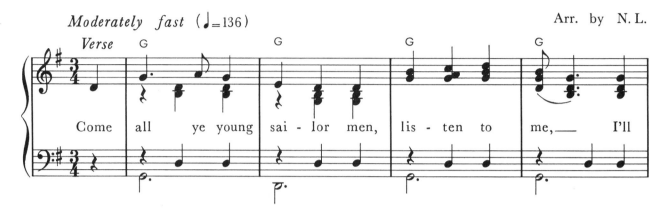

Verse
Come all ye young sai - lor men, lis - ten to me, —— I'll

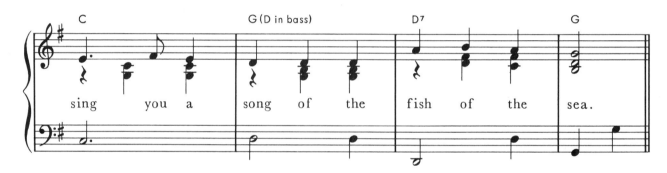

sing you a song of the fish of the sea.

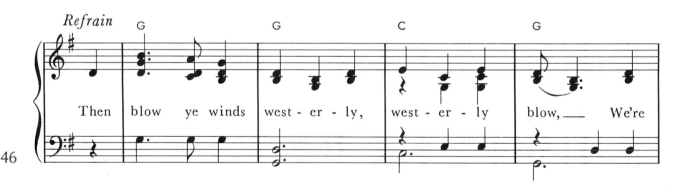

Refrain
Then blow ye winds west - er - ly, west - er - ly blow, —— We're

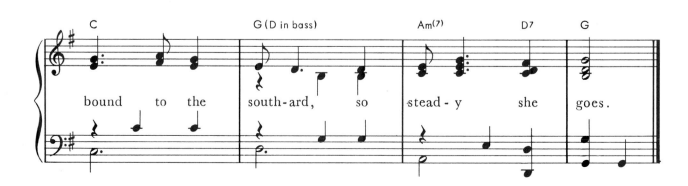

bound to the south-ard, so stead - y she goes.

46

2. Oh, first come the whale, the biggest of all.
   He climbed up aloft and let ev'ry sail fall.
   Refrain

3. Next come the smelt, the smallest of all.
   He jumped to the poop and sung out, "Tops'l haul."
   Refrain

4. The herring come, sayin' "I'm king of the seas.
   If you want any wind, why I'll blow you a breeze."
   Refrain

5. And last come the flounder, as flat as the ground.
   He says, "Blast your eyes, chuckle-head, mind how you sound."
   Refrain

TEN THOUSAND CATTLE

This "lament" is known by many titles and sung to many tunes. Our version is from the singing of Arthur Craxton in Chicago in 1935.

STRUM: VIB or IIB

UNITED STATES

Arr. by N. L.

Moderately slow (♩ = 63)

Verse

1. Ten thou-sand cat-tle___ gone a-stray, Left my range and trav-eled a-way, And the sons of guns, I'm here to say, Have left me a dead broke, dead broke to-day.___

2. And now my gal___ has gone a-way Left my home and trav-eled a-way, With a son-of-a-gun from I-o-way, Left me a lone man, lone man to-day.___

Refrain

In gam-bling hells de-lay-ing, Ten thou-sand cat-tle stray-ing,___ Ten thou-sand cat-tle stray-ing.___

48

LOVE SONGS TENDER

49

ONE MAN SHALL MOW MY MEADOW

STRUM: Vb

A lovely, free-form cumulative song. It is safe to assume that the text has cryptic overtones.

ENGLAND

Arr. by N. L.

Moderately (♩ = 132)

One man shall mow my mead-ow, ____ Two

men   shall   ga - ther   it   to - geth - er. _____

* E   B7   E   B7   E   G#m

Two   men,   one   man,   and   one   more   Shall

C#m   A   F#m   F#m

shear   my   lambs   and   ewes   and   rams, _____

F#m   E   B7   E

_____   And   gath - er   my   gold   to - geth - er. _____

* Repeat as necessary.

2. Three men shall mow my meadow.
    Four men shall gather it together.
    Four men, three men, *two men, one man, etc.*

3. Five men shall mow my meadow.
    Six men shall gather it together.
    Six men, five men, *four men, three men, etc.*

4. Seven men shall mow my meadow.
    Eight men shall gather it together.
    Eight men, seven men, *etc.*

5. Nine men shall mow my meadow.
    Ten men shall gather it together.
    Ten men, nine men, *etc.*

GYPSY ROVER

This song and the next three are similar in story-line and quality: "the maid who would give up all for love!"

STRUM: IA or VA

IRELAND

Arr. by N. L.

Moderately (♩=132)

The gyp-sy ro-ver came o-ver the hill, Bound thru the val-ley so

sha — dy; He whis-tled and he sang till the green woods rang, And

52

he won the heart of a la — — dy. _____

Refrain

Lah-dee-o, lah-dee -o-ah-day, Lah-dee-o, lah-dee-

ay - dee. He whis-tled and he sang till the green woods rang, And

he won the heart of a la - - dy.

2. She left her father's castle gate,
   She left her own true lover;
   She left her servants and her estate,
   To follow the gypsy rover.
   Lahdeeo, ladeeoahday,
   Lahdeeo, ladeeaydee,
   She left her servants, *etc*.

3. Her father saddled his fastest steed,
   He roam'd the valley all over;
   He sought his daughter at great speed,
   And the whistling gypsy rover.
   Lahdeeo, lahdeeoahday,
   Lahdeeo, lahdeeaydee,
   He sought his daughter, *etc*.

4. He came at last to a mansion fine,
   Down by the River Claydee;
   And there was music, and there was wine,
   For the gypsy and his lady.
   Lahdeeo, lahdeeoahday,
   Lahdeeo, lahdeeaydee,
   And there was music, *etc*.

5. "O, father he's no gypsy free,
   But lord of lands all over;
   And I will stay till my dying day,
   With my whistling gypsy rover."
   Lahdeeo, lahdeeoahday,
   Lahdeeo, lahdeeaydee,
   "And I will stay," *etc*.

53

THE GIPSUM DAVY

An American version of
the English "Raggle Taggle
Gypsies."

STRUM: XA or IA

UNITED STATES

Arr. by N. L.

Moderately ($\bullet = 84$)

Verse

It was late in the night when the squire came home, En-quir-ing for his la-dy. His

ser-vant gave a sure re-ply, "She's gone with the Gip-sum Da-vy".

Refrain

Rat-tle tum a Gip-sum, Gip-sum, Rat-tle tum a

54

Gip-sum Da-vy, ____

1.

2.

Da-vy.

2. "O, go catch up my milkwhite steed,
   The black one's not so speedy.
   I'll ride all night till broad daylight,
   Or overtake my lady."
   Refrain:

3. He rode and he rode till he came to town,
   He rode till he came to Barley.
   The tears came a–rolling down his cheeks,
   And there he spied his lady.
   Refrain:

4. It's "Come back home, my dearest dear,
   O, come back home my honey,
   It's "Come go back my dearest dear,
   And you never shall lack for money."
   Refrain:

5. "I won't go back my dearest dear,
   I won't go back my honey,
   For I wouldn't give a kiss from the gypsy's lips
   For you and all your money."
   Refrain:

6. It's "Go pull off those snow–white gloves
   All made of Spanish leather,
   And give to me your lily–white hand,
   And bid farewell forever."
   Refrain:

7. Now she pull'd off those snow–white gloves,
   All made of Spanish leather,
   And gave to him her lily–white hand,
   And bade farewell forever.
   Refrain:

8. She soon ran through her gay clothing,
   Her velvet shoes and stockings;
   Her gold ring off her finger's gone,
   And the gold plate off her bosom.
   Refrain:

9. "O, once I had a house and land,
   A feather bed and money;
   But now I've come to an old straw pad,
   With the gypsies dancing 'round me."
   Refrain:

55

THE COLLIER LADDIE

The tenderest of love songs
from Aberdeenshire.

STRUM: I-A

SCOTLAND

Arr. by N. L.

Moderately slow (♩ = 92)

56

C | Em | F | C

Oh,— I've been east and I've been— west, And

C | Am | Dm⁷ G⁷ C | C | G⁷

I've been in Kirk-cal-dy; But the bon-ni-est las-sie that

Am F G⁷ | C | F C | Dm⁷ G⁷ C

e-ver I saw, She was fol-low-ing a col-lier lad-die.

2. "O,   where live ye, my bonnie lass?
   And   tell me what they ca' ye?"
"Bonnie   Jeanie Gordon is my name,
   And I'm following my collier laddie."

3. "O,   see ye not yon hills and dales
   The   sun shines on sae brawlie;
   They   a' are mine, and they'll be thine,
Gin ye'll leave your collier laddie.

4. And   ye shall busk in gay attire,
   Weel   busket up sae brawlie;
   And   ane to wait on ev'ry hand,
Gin ye'll leave your collier laddie."

5. "Tho   ye had a' the sun shines on,
   And the earth conceals sae lowly,
   I would turn my back on you and it a',
   And em — brace my collier laddie.

6. O,   I can win my five pennies a day,
   And   spend at night fu' brawlie;
   And   make my bed in the collier's neuk,
   And lie doon wi' my collier laddie."

7. O,   love for love's the bargain for me,
   Tho the wee cot house should haud me;
   And the warld before me to win my bread,
   And   fair fa' my collier laddie."

I KNOW WHERE I'M GOING

"Some say he's black, but I say he's bonnie" seems to indicate that the young man was a collier laddie. The "Dear" refers to the dear Lord.

STRUM: IX

SCOTLAND

Arr. by N. L.

2. I have stockings of silk,
   And shoes of bright green leather,
   Combs to buckle me hair,
   And a ring for ev'ry finger.

3. Feather beds are soft,
   And painted rooms are bonny,
   But I would leave them all,
   For my handsome winsome Johnny.

4. Some say he's black,
   But I say he's bonny;
   Fairest of them all,
   Is my handsome winsome Johnny.
   Repeat first verse.

MI CABALLO BLANCO

In this song, a man's best friend is his "Caballo Blanco" (white horse).

STRUM: II-B or XII-B

CHILE

Arr. by N. L.

Moderately slow (♩ = 116)

Verse

Es mi ca- ba- llo blan - co
com-o un a - man - e - cer, Siem - pre jun - ti - tos
va - mos, es mi_a - mi - go mas fi - el.

Refrain

1. Mi ca-ballo,   mi ca-ballo,   go-lo pan-do   va.
2. Mi ca-ballo,   mi ca-ballo,   se va y se   va.

59

Ah _____

rit.

SEARCHING FOR LAMBS

A gentle ballad which, because of the 5/4 meter, gives the lie to those who say that folk music is too simple.

STRUM: IX

ENGLAND

Arr. by N. L.

Freely (♩ = 126)

As I went out one May morn-ing, One
May morn-ing be-time, I met a maid, from
home had strayed, Just as the sun did shine.

2. "What makes you rise so soon, my dear,
　　Your journey to pursue?
　　Your pretty little feet, they tread so neat.
　　Strike off the morning dew."

3. "I'm going to feed my father's flock,
　　His young and tender lambs,
　　That over hills and over dales
　　Lie waiting for their dams."

4. "Oh stay, oh stay, you handsome maid,
　　And rest a moment here,
　　For there is none but you alone
　　That I do love so dear."

5. "How gloriously the sun doth shine,
　　How pleasant is the air.
　　I'd rather rest on a true love's breast
　　Than any other where."

6. "For I am thine and thou art mine.
　　No man shall uncomfort thee.
　　We'll join our hands in wedded bands
　　And a–married we will be."

WILL YE GO, LASSIE?

Known also as "Wild Mountain Thyme," it's a beautifully simple and poetic text.

STRUM: IX

IRELAND

Freely (♩=66)

Arr. by N. L.

Verse

Oh, the sum-mer time is com-ing, And the trees are sweet-ly bloom-ing, And the wild moun-tain thyme ____ Grows a-round the bloom-ing hea-ther. Will ye go, ____ las-sie, go?

Refrain

And we'll all go to-geth-er, To pluck

62

wild moun-tain thyme,____ All a-round the bloom-ing heath-er. Will ye go,____ las-sie, go?

2. I will build my love a tower.
   Near yon pure crystal fountain,
   And on it I will build.
   All the flowers of the mountain.
   Will ye go, lassie, go?
   Refrain:

3. If my true love she were gone.
   I would surely find another,
   Where the wild mountain thyme
   Grows around the blooming heather,
   Will ye go, lassie, go?
   Refrain:

4. Repeat 1st verse and refrain

HANGMAN

Rejection and ransom—these are the basis for many folk tales. In this Ozark variant of the great Child ballad, true love succeeds when all else has failed.

STRUM: IIA or VI-A

UNITED STATES

Moderately fast ($\quarternote$ = 152)

Arr. by N. L.

"Hang-man, hang-man, slack up your rope, Slack it for a while. I

look o-ver yon-der and I see my Paw a-com-in', He's walked for ma-ny a

mile." "Say Paw, say Paw, have you brung me an-y gold, An-y

64

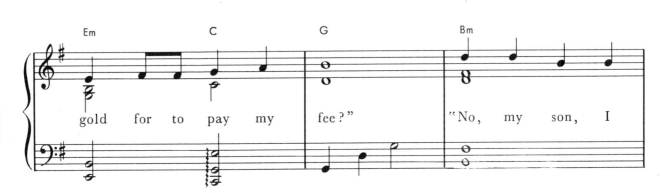

gold for to pay my fee?" "No, my son, I

have-n't an-y gold; You must hang on the gal-lows—— tree."

In verses 2, 3, 4, and 5, substitute "ma", "sister", "brother", "cousin", and so on, repeating entire verse each time.

LAST VERSE

"Hangman, hangman, slack up your rope,
Slack it for a while.
I think I see my true love comin',
She's walk'd for many a mile."
"Say love, say love, have you brung me any gold,
Any gold for to pay my fee?"
"Yes, I have brung you yeller, yeller gold,
To take you home with me."

65

THE RANSOMED SOLDIER

A Polish version of the same story as
"Hangman" with a tune of great bravura.

STRUM: IVA or IA

POLAND

Eng Version by W. S.
Arr. by N. L.

Moderately (♩ = 92)

Jail - er, Oh, jail - er, please take this let - ter home for me.

Tell them I must be ran - somed or I shall ne'er go free.

1. "Jail — er O, jail — er, please take this let — ter home for me. . . . .
   Tell them I must be ran — somed or I shall ne'er go free." . . . .

66

2. "Fa — ther, O, fa — ther, please sell your fine black hors—es three, ...
   So I can pay my ran — som, for then I shall go free." . . . .

3. "How can I sell my black hors — es three to ran — som thee? . . . .
   I can — not use my ox — en to pull my coach for me!" . . . .

4. *Repeat verse 1.*

5. "True love, O, true love, please sell your sil — ver rings for me, ...
   So I can pay my ran — som, for then I shall go free." . . . .

6. "Yes, my be — lov — ed, I've sold my sil — ver rings for thee. . . . .
   Now pay your ran — som and quick—ly come back home to me!" . . . .

SAKURA

Nowhere is the charm of Japan better illustrated than in a song such as "Sakura"— delicate and poetic, but so typically formal.

JAPAN
English lyrics by Marilyn Keith and Alan Bergman
Arr. by N. L.

STRUM: VIA or IIA

Slowly (♩ = 64)

Sa - ku - ra,   Sa - ku - ra,   Ten - der blos - som
Sa - ku - ra,   Sa - ku - ra,   Ya - yo - i   no

born of___ spring,   Sired by win - ter's   gen - tle___ snow,
So - ra - wa,   Mi - wa - ta - su   ka - gi - ri,

Once a - gain you   bless my___ eyes,   Would love thus re - turn to___ me.
Ka - su - mi ka   ku - mo - ka   Ni - o - i   zo   i - zu - ru

Sa - ku - ra,   Sa - ku - ra,   Would love thus re - turn___ to   me.
I - za - ya,   I - za - ya,   Mi___   ni   yu - ka - un.

67

* Guitar : Omit third in E chord throughout (no G or G♯)

LOVELY MOON

A poetic lyrical setting of an early nineteenth
century melody.

GERMANY
Eng. Version by W. S.
Arr. by N. L.

STRUM: VA

68

lov - er will dis - cov - er All the joy the shin - ing moon can
fol - gen mei - ne Bli - cke dei - ner stil - len, hei - tern___

bring as he sings: Love - ly moon, you shine so bright - ly
Bahn: ___ O, wie hart ist das___ Ge ___

in the sky, Like a lamp of sil - ver rid - ing high.
schi - cke, dass ich dir nicht fol - gen___ kann.

2. Lovely   moon, the scholars say you help the sun,
Make the tides of oceans ebb and flow.
Surely   you can move the heart of my dear one,
As she   gazes on your silvry glow.
Stop and hover right above her,
And re — flect love's message I would bring, as I sing:
Lovely   moon, you shine so brightly, etc.

69

VALENCIANITA

A lovely example of the alternating 6/8 and 3/4
meters so common in Latin-American music.

STRUM: VIII

VENEZUELA

English lyrics by Marilyn Keith
and Alan Bergman
Arr. by N. L.

Gaily ♪= 216

Refrain

U-na Va-len-cia- ni - ta,   like the or-ange of   Spain,
U-na Va-len-cia- ni - ta,   que del cie-lo ba- jo

You are gold as the sun - shine,   you are sweet as the rain,
Con el pe-lo ex-ten- di - do   y en la bo-ca u-na flor,

Like a beau-ti-ful or - ange   on the tree high a - bove,
En la flor u-na ro - sa,   en la ro-sa un cla- vel,

70

U-na Va-len-cia-ni - ta,
yEn la ma-no u-na ni - na

can I reach you, my love.
que se lla-ma I-sa - bel.

Verse

Wo-man of sun-ny Va-len - cia,
I - sa - be-li - ta me lla - mo,

come to the win-dow, I pray.
hi - ja soy de un-la-bra - dor;

Smile at me just for a mo - ment,
Aun - que voy y voy al cam - po

please do not send me a - way.
no le ten-go mie-do al sol.

Refrain 2. Una Valencianita,
Like the orange of Spain,
You are gold as the sunshine.
You are sweet as the rain.
Like the fairest of blossoms
Blooming high on the vine,
Una Valencianita,
Will you ever be mine?

Verse 2. Woman of sunny Valencia,
Loveliest woman I see,
I will wait under your window
Till you come dancing with me.
Refrain

2. Esta rueda es mi jardin
Y las niñas son las rosas,
Y yo, como jardinera,
Escojo la mas hermoso.
Refrain

71

MARIANNI

The source of this song is unknown but it's thought to be of Neapolitan origin.
A sad but amusing "lover's complaint."

ITALY

English lyrics by Marilyn Keith
and Alan Bergman
Arr. by N. L.

STRUM: IX

Freely (♩ = 72)

1. Ma - ri - an - ni, there's a moon a - bove,
2. Ma - ri - an - ni, on a night like this,

And you know what I am think - ing of.
Not a pre - cious mo - ment should we miss.

STRUM: IA

Start with slow tempo and gradually get faster

Yet when I be - gin to speak of love,
Yet when - ev - er we're a - bout to kiss,

Ma - ri - an - ni, how you laugh. What is there to make you

72

73

2. Marianni, on a night like this,
   Not a precious moment should we miss.
   Yet whenever we're about to kiss,
   Marianni, how you laugh!
   What is there to make you laugh?
   Won't you tell me why you laugh?
   Mariannina, laugh no more,
   You're the one that I adore.
   Mariannina, can't you see,
   You're the only one for me.

MY LAGAN LOVE

A beautiful modal tune from Ulster. The tune is traditional, though this text was added early in the twentieth century.

STRUM: Vʙ or IIʙ

IRELAND

Arr. by N. L.

Slowly (♩ = 50)

Where La - gan stream sings lull - a - by There blows a li - ly fair. The twi - light___ gleam is in her eye, The

74

night____ is on her hair. And like a love-sick *len-an-

shee She____ hath my heart____ in thrall, Nor life I

owe nor lib-er-ty, For love____-is lord of all.

2. And   often when the beetle's horn
   Hath   lulled the eve to sleep,
   I   steal unto her shieling lorn
   And   thru the dooring peep.
   There on the cricket's singing stone,
   She   spares the bogwood fire.
   And   hums in sad sweet undertone
   The   song of heart's desire.

3. Her   welcome, like her love for me,
   Is   from her heart within.
   Her   warm kiss is felicity
   That   knows no taint of sin,
   And   when I stir my foot to go,
   'Tis   leaving love and light
   To   feel the wind of longing blow
   From   out the dark of night.

75

* Fairy mistress

4. *Repeat first verse.*

MY LITTLE MOHEE

The ancestor of "On Top of old Smoky," and a lovely melody in its own right.

STRUM: IIIB or IIB

UNITED STATES

Moderately (♩ = 140)

Arr. by N. L.

As I went out walk-ing ———— a - lone one fine day, ———— I got aw - ful lone-some, ———— as the day passed a - way. ———— As I sat a - mus-ing ———— a - lone on the grass, ———— When who should walk by me ———— but a sweet In - dian lass. ——

2. She came and sat by me,
And took hold of my hand.
Said: "You sure be a stranger
In a far, strange land."
She asked me to marry,
And offered her hand.
Said: "My pappy's a chieftain
All over this land."

3. "My pappy's a chieftain
And a ruler be he.
I'm his only daughter,
And my name is Mohee."
I answered and told her
That it never could be,
'Cause I had a dear sweetheart
In my own countree.

4. "I will not forsake her
For I know she loves me.
Her heart is as true as
Any Mohee.
So I'm going to leave you,
Now farewell, my dear.
There's wind in my canvas,
To my home I must steer."

5. At home with relations
I tried for to see,
But there wasn't a one like
My little Mohee.
And the girl I had trusted
Prov'd untrue to me,
So I sail'd back o'er the ocean
To my lovely Mohee.

CARMEN, CARMELA

Although this sounds much like a composed song, it is widely known and sung as a folk song throughout Mexico.

MEXICO

English lyrics by Marilyn Keith
and Alan Bergman
Arr. by N. L.

STRUM: XIIA

Moderately (♩ = 96)

Refrain   D (A in bass)   A⁷   A⁷   D

Car - men, Car - me - la,   Oh, my be - lov - ed,
Car - men, Car - me - la,   *Luz de mis o - jos*

78

D   A⁷   A⁷   D

You are the sun - light   that warms the day.
Si luz no hu - bie - ra   *ha - bías de ser.*

79

TENDER LOVE

In the Cajun country, this is sometimes sung as a lullaby.

STRUM: VA or IA

UNITED STATES

Slowly (♩ = 63)

Eng. lyric and Arr. by N. L.

Love,   love,   ten - der   love,
Love,   love,   ten - der   love,

Where   are   you   to - night? _____ Moon and   stars   shine from a -
Hear   my   lone - ly   cry. _____ Moon and   stars   die up a -

bove,   But with - out you, there is   no   light.
bove,   And with - out you, then so   will   I.

LOVE SONGS TRAGIC

THE FOUR MARYS

The story of Mary Hamilton, supposed to be one of four ladies-in-waiting to Mary, Queen of Scots, known as the "4 Maries." The appealing text and melody somehow transcend the song's historical inaccuracy.

STRUM: VI-B

SCOTLAND

Arr. by N. L.

Slowly, but with movement ($\quarternote$=100)

Last night there were four Ma - rys, This
night there'll be but three; There were
Ma - ry Bea - ton, and Ma - ry Sea - ton, And
Ma - ry Car - mi - chael and me.

82

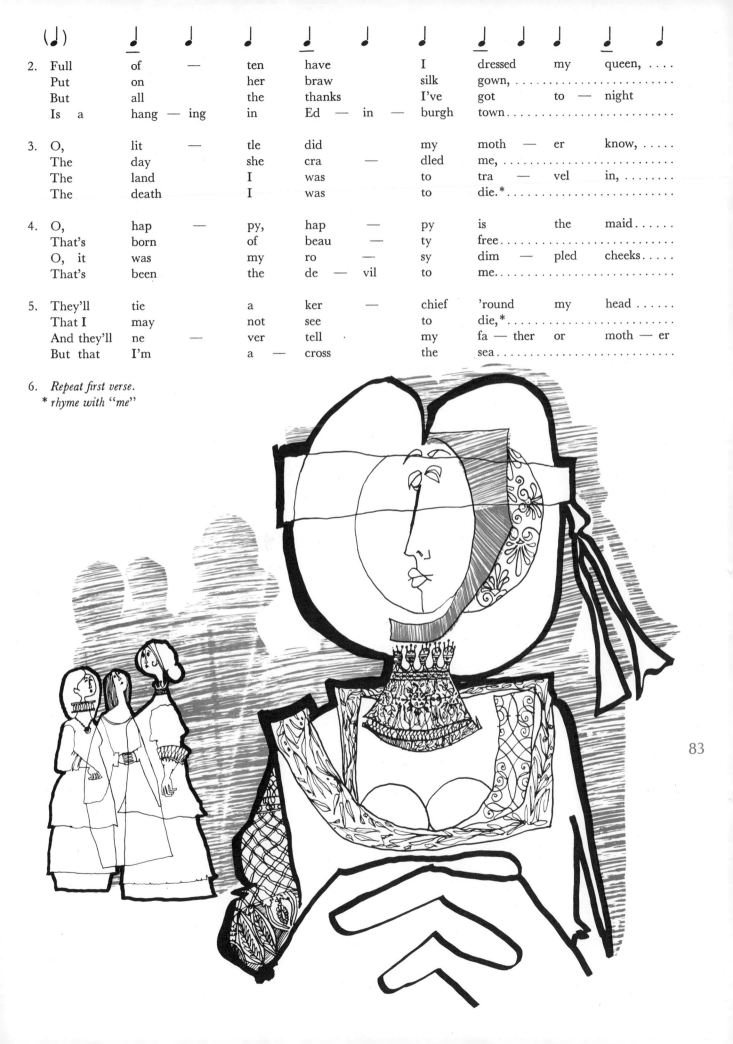

(♩) ♩ ♩ ♩ ♩ ♩ ♩ ♩ ♩ ♩ ♩ ♩

2. Full of — ten have I dressed my queen, ...
Put on her braw silk gown, ...
But all the thanks I've got to — night
Is a hang — ing in Ed — in — burgh town . . . .

3. O, lit — tle did my moth — er know, ...
The day she cra — dled me, ...
The land I was to tra — vel in, ...
The death I was to die.* . . . .

4. O, hap — py, hap — py is the maid . . . . . .
That's born of beau — ty free . . . .
O, it was my ro — sy dim — pled cheeks . . . . .
That's been the de — vil to me. . . . .

5. They'll tie a ker — chief 'round my head . . . . . .
That I may not see to die,* . . . .
And they'll ne — ver tell my fa — ther or moth — er
But that I'm a — cross the sea . . . .

6. *Repeat first verse.*
   * *rhyme with "me"*

83

LORD RENDALL

The great diversity of folk songs which stem from a
common source is wonderfully demonstrated in the next
four songs. The same story in one version causes terror, in the next lulls a child to sleep.
In one version we see the lethal effects of roasted eel, in another the delectable taste of cherry pie.

STRUM: VIB

UNITED STATES

Arr. by N. L.

Moderately slow (♩ = 88)

"Oh,— where have you been,— Lord— Ren - dall, my son? Oh,—

where have you been,— my own— dear - est one?" "Oh,—

84

I've been a - court - ing, Mother. Make my bed soon, For I'm sick to the ___ heart, and I fain would lie down."

(♩)

2. "What had you for sup — per, Lord Ren — dall, my son? . . .
   What had you for sup — per, my own dear—est one?" . .
   "Some eels fried in bat — ter, Moth — er. Make my bed soon, . . .
   For I'm sick to the heart, and I fain would lie doon." . .

3. "And what were their col — or, Lord Ren — dall, my son? . . . .
   And what were their col — or, my own dear—est one?"
   "They were black, white, and yel — low, Moth — er. Make my bed soon, . . .
   For I'm sick to the heart, and I fain would lie doon." .

4. "What will you leave your fath — er, Lord Ren — dall, my son? . . . .
   What will you leave your fath — er, my own dear—est one?" . .
   "A black suit of mourn — ing, Moth — er. Make my bed soon, . . .
   For I'm sick to the heart, and I fain would lie doon." . .

5. "What will you leave your moth — er, Lord Ren — dall, my son? . . . .
   What will you leave your moth — er, my own dear—est one?" . . . 85
   "A coach and six hor — ses, Moth — er. Make my bed soon, . . .
   For I'm sick to the heart, and I fain would lie doon." . .

6. "What will you leave your broth — er, Lord Ren — dall, my son? . . . .
   What will you leave your broth — er, my own dear—est one?" . . .
   "A black yoke of ox — en, Moth — er. Make my bed soon, . . .
   For I'm sick to the heart, and I fain would lie doon." . _

7. "What will you leave your sweet — heart, Lord Ren — dall, my son? . . . .
   What will you leave your sweet — heart, my own dear—est one?" . . .
   "Ten thou—sand weights of brim — stone to burn her bones brown . .
   For she was the cause of my ly — ing doon." .

LITTLE WEE CROODIN DOO

An adaptation of the same tale for the nursery.

STRUM: IB

ENGLAND

Arr. by N. L.

Not too fast (♩.= 52)

"Oh, where have you been all this live-long day, My

lit - tle wee croo - din doo?" "I've

been to see my step - moth - er, Dear

Mom - my, oh, make my bed noo".

86

♩ (♪) ♪ ♪ ♪ ♪ ♪ ♪ ♪ ♪ ♪ ♪

2. "And what did your step—moth—er give you to eat, ...
My lit — tle wee croo — din doo?"................
"She gave me but a wee, wee fish, ...
All cov — er'd with green and blue."..............

3. "And what did you do with the bones of the fish, ...
My lit — tle wee croo — din doo?"................
"I gave them to my wee, wee dog ....
Dear Mom — my, O, make my bed noo."................

4. "And what did your dog when he ate up the bones, ..
My lit — tle wee croo — din doo?"................
"He stretch'd his wee, wee limbs and died, ...
Dear Mom — my, as I do noo."................

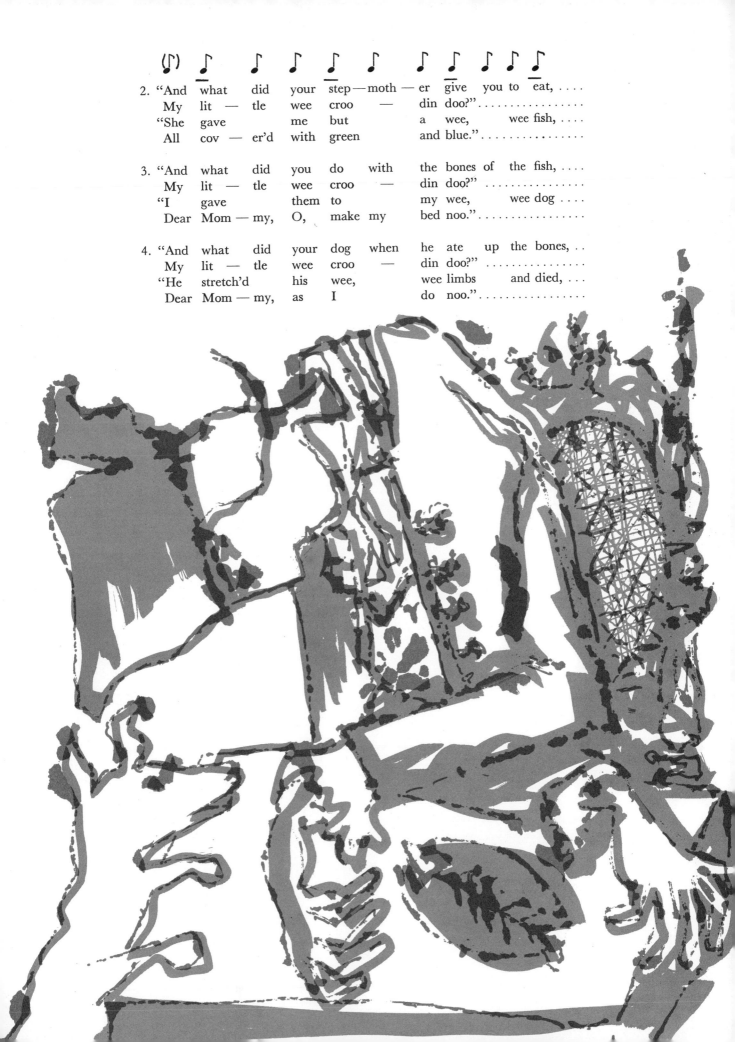

MY BOY WILLIE

STRUM: Ic

ENGLAND
Arr. by N. L.

Lively (♩=112)

"Oh, where have you been all the day, My boy Wil - lie?___ Oh,

where have you been all the day? Oh, Wil - lie, won't you tell me now?"

88

"I've been all the day court - ing of a la - dy gay,

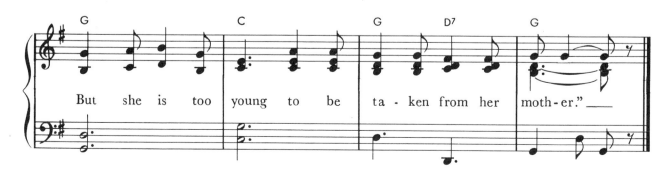

But she is too young to be ta - ken from her moth - er."___

2. "O, can she brew, and can she bake,
   My boy Willie?
   O, can she brew and can she bake?
   O, Willie won't you tell me now?"
"She can brew, and she can bake.
She can make a wedding cake,
But she is too young," *etc*.

3. "O, can she knit, and can she spin,
   My boy Willie?
   O, can she knit, and can she spin?
   O, Willie won't you tell me now?"
"She can knit, and she can spin;
She can do most any thing,
But she is too young," *etc*.

4. "O, how old is she now,
   My boy Willie?
   O, how old is she now?
   O, Willie won't you tell me now?"
"Two times six, two times seven,
Two times twenty and eleven,
But she is too young," *etc*.

THE SPECKLED FISH

More like "Lord Rendall" than the others, even in the bequest to his sweetheart.

Strum: IX

GERMANY
Eng. Version by W. S.

Freely ($\text{\textonehalf}$ = 63)

Where have you been this live long day, Hen - ry my dear-est son? "I've
Wo bist du denn so lang ge - wes'n, Hei - ne-rich, mein lie - ber Sohn?"Ich

90

been with my true love all the day, Oh Moth - er, ease my pain! From
bin bei meinem Feins - lieb - chen ge - wes'n, Frau Mutt - er mein, o weh! Mein

some dark__ po - tion My young life ebbs a - way".
jun - ges__ Leb - en Ver - ge - ben hat sie's mir".

2. "What kind of food did she prepare,
    Henry, my dearest son?"
   "She cooked a long and speckled fish.
    Oh, Mother, ease my pain.
    From some dark potion
    My young life ebbs away."

3. "How many portions did she serve,
    Henry, my dearest son?"
   "Just three small portions did she serve.
    Oh, Mother," *etc.*

4. "To whom was the third portion giv'n,
    Henry, my dearest son?"
   "She gave it to her little dog.
    Oh, Mother," *etc.*

5. "And what befell her little dog,
    Henry, my dearest son?"
   "His belly burst before my eyes.
    Oh, Mother," *etc.*

6. "What do you wish your father dear,
    Henry, my dearest son?"
   "A thousand blessings on his head.
    Oh, Mother," *etc.*

7. "What do you wish your mother dear,
    Henry, my dearest son?"
   "I wish for you eternal bliss.
    Oh, Mother," *etc.*

8. "What do you wish your own true love?
    Henry, my dearest son?"
   "I wish her flames and torment of Hell.
    Oh, Mother," *etc.*

2. „Was gab sie dir zu essen?
    Heinerich, mein lieber Sohn!"
   „Sie kocht mir einen bunten Fisch,
    Frau Mutter mein, O weh!
    Mein junges Leben,
    Vergeben hat sie's mir."

3. „Und wie viel Stücke schnitt sie dir?
    Heinerich, mein lieber Sohn!"
   „Sie schnitt davon drei Stückelein,
    Frau Mutter mein", *etc.*

4. „Wo liess sie denn das dritte Stück?
    Heinerich, mein lieber Sohn!"
   „Sie gab's ihren schwarzbraunen Hündelein,
    Frau Mutter mein", *etc.*

5. „Und was geschah dem Hündelein?
    Heinerich, mein lieber Sohn!"
   „Der Bauch sprang ihm in der Mitt entzwei,
    Frau Mutter mein", *etc.*

6. „Was wünschest du deinem Vater?
    Heinerich, mein lieber Sohn!"
   „Ich wünsch ihm tausend Glück un Segn,
    Frau Mutter mein", *etc.*

7. „Was wünschest du deiner Mutter?
    Heinerich, mein lieber Sohn!"
   „Ich wünsch ihr die ewige Seligheit,
    Frau Mutter mein", *etc.*

8. „Was wünschest du deiner Liebsten?
    Heinerich, mein lieber Sohn!"
   „Ich wünsch ihr die ewige Höll und Qual,
    Frau Mutter mein", *etc.*

THE BONNY EARL OF MURRAY

Suspected of plotting rebellion against James VI of Scotland, Murray was "unmercifully slain."
Popular feelings ran so high, the court had to be moved to Glasgow.

SCOTLAND

STRUM: IIIB or IB

Slowly, but with movement ($\quad$ = 66)

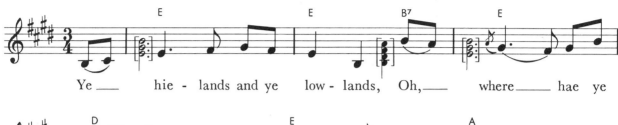

Ye ___ hie - lands and ye low - lands, Oh, ___ where ___ hae ye

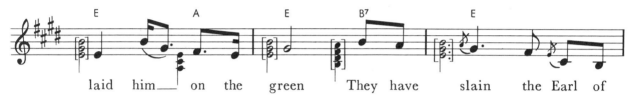

been? ___ They have slain the Earl of Mur - ray, And they

laid him ___ on the green They have slain the Earl of

Mur - ray, And they laid him ___ on the green. ___

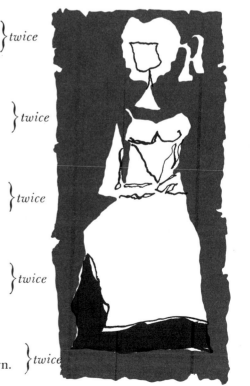

2. Now woe be to thee, Huntley!
   And wherefore did you say?
   I bade you bring him wi' you,
   But forbade you him to slay. } *twice*

3. He was a braw gallant,
   And he rode at the ring;
   And the bonny Earl of Murray,
   Oh, he might have been a king. } *twice*

4. He was a braw gallant,
   And he play'd at the ba';
   And the bonny Earl of Murray
   Was the flower among them a'. } *twice*

5. He was a braw gallant,
   And he play'd at the glove;
   And the bonny Earl of Murray,
   Oh, he was the Queen's love. } *twice*

6. Oh! long will his lady
   Look o'er the castle down
   Ere she see the Earl of Murray
   Come sounding through the town. } *twice*

GEORDIE

Had his lady love but been there to fight for him, perhaps Geordie would not have been caught and hanged "in golden chains."

STRUM: IX

ENGLAND

Arr. by N. L.

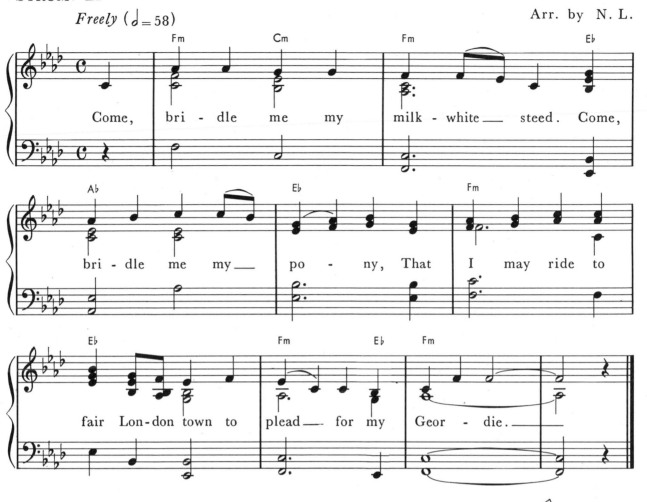

Freely (♩ = 58)

Come, bri - dle me my milk - white___ steed. Come, bri - dle me my___ po - ny, That I may ride to fair Lon-don town to plead___ for my Geor - die.

2. And when he enter'd in the hall, there were lords and ladies plenty.
Down on her knees, she then did fall, to plead for the life of Geordie.

3. Then Geordie look'd around the court, and saw his dearest Polly.
He said, "My dear, you've come too late, for I'm condemn'd already."

4. The judge then looked down on him, and said, "I'm sorry for thee.
Thine own confession hath hangéd thee. May the Lord have mercy on thee."

5. O, Geordie stole no cow or calf, and he never murdered any,
But he stole sixteen of the king's white steeds, and sold them in Bohenny.

6. Let Geordie hang in golden chains, (his crimes were never many),
Because he came from royal blood, and courted a virtuous lady.

7. I wish I was in yonder grove, where times I have been many.
With my broad sword and pistol too, I'd fight for the life of Geordie.

93

BARB'RA ELLEN

Scottish in origin, this English variant is almost identical with an American version from West Virginia.

STRUM: IIB or VI-B

ENGLAND

Arr. by N. L.

Slowly (♩= 60)

In Scar-let Town where I was born, There was a fair maid dwel-lin'; Made ev'-ry youth cry,— well-a-day! And her name was Bar-b'ra El-len.

94

2. 'Twas in the merry month of May,
   When green buds they were swellin'.
   Sweet William on his deathbed lay
   For the love of Barb'ra Ellen.

3. He sent a servant to the town,
   To the place where she was dwellin'.
   "My master's sick and he bids you come
   If your name be Barb'ra Ellen."

4. Then slowly, slowly she got up,
   And slowly she went nigh him;
   And as she drew the curtain back:
   "Young man, I think you're dyin!"

5. "O, ken you not in yonder town,
   In the place where we were dwellin',
   You gave a health to the ladies all,
   But you slighted Barb'ra Ellen."

6. "O, yes I ken. I ken it well.
   In the place where we were dwellin',
   I gave a health to the ladies all,
   But my love to Barb'ra Ellen."

7. Then slowly went she down the stairs.
   He trembled like an aspen.
   "Be kind, good friends and neighbors all,
   Be kind to Barb'ra Ellen."

8. And as she cross'd the wooded fields,
   She heard his deathbell knellin',
   And ev'ry stroke, it spoke her name
   "Hard-hearted Barb'ra Ellen."

9. She look'd to the east, she looked to the west.
   She saw his corpse a–comin'.
   "O, bearers, bearers, lay him down,
   For I think I too am dyin'."

10. "O, Mother, Mother, make my bed,
    And make it long and narrow.
    Sweet William died for the love of me;
    I'll die for him of sorrow!"

11. "O, Father, Father, dig my grave,
    And dig it deep and narrow.
    Sweet William died for me today.
    I'll die for him tomorrow."

12. They buried her in the old churchyard.
    They buried him beside her,
    And from his heart grew a red, red rose,
    And from her heart a briar.

13. They climb'd right up the old church wall
    Till they couldn't climb no higher.
    They tied themselves in a true lovers' knot;
    The red rose 'round the briar.

I NEVER WILL MARRY

A very lonesome tune
with a touching story—
almost a blues song.

STRUM: IIIB

UNITED STATES

Moderately (♩=120)

Arr. by N. L.

Verse 1. One morn-ing I ram-bled down by the sea-
I heard some fair maid-en give a pit-i-ful

Refrain I nev-er will mar-ry, I'll be no man's
The shells of the o-cean Shall be my death

shore, The wind it did whis-tle,
cry, And it sound-ed so lone-ly,
wife, I in-tend to live sin-gle
bed, While the fish in deep wa-ter

and the wa-ters did roar.
as it swept off on high.
All the days of my life.
Swim o-ver my head.

96

Refrain—same tune as verse
"I never will marry,
I'll be no man's wife.
I intend to live single
All the days of my life.
The shells in the ocean
Shall be my death bed,
While the fish in deep water
Swim over my head."

2. She cast her fair body
In the water so deep,
And she closed her pretty blue eyes
Forever to sleep.
So now as I wander
Down by the seaside,
I weep for that fair one
Who sang as she died:
Refrain:

LOVE SONGS BITTERSWEET

97

THE DARK-EYED SAILOR

Songs of delayed recognition
abound in folklore. This broadside
ballad has a particularly beautiful
modal tune.

STRUM: II-A or V-A

UNITED STATES

Arr. by N. L.

Slowly ($\downarrow$ = 63)

98

'Twas of a maid both young and fair, Whil'st walk-ing out for to take the

air. She met a sail-or all on her way, And I paid at-

ten-tion, and I paid at-ten-tion,____ To hear what they might say.

2. He says, "Fair maid, why roam alone?
    For the day's far spent, and night's coming on."
    While crystal tears from her eyes did flow:
    "It's my dark-eyed sailor, oh, my dark-eyed sailor,
    That proved my overthrow."

3. "'Tis three long years since he left this land.
    A new gold ring he took off his hand.
    He broke this token, gave half to me,
    While the other half's lying, the other half's lying
    At the bottom of the sea."

4. "Oh," he says, "Fair maid, drive him off your mind,
    For as good a sailor as him you'll find!
    Love turns aside, and cold does grow
    Like a winter's morning, like a winter's morning,
    When the hills are cover'd with snow."

5. "His coal-black eyes and curly hair,
    His flatt'ring tongue did my heart ensnare.
    Genteel he was, no rake like you,
    To advise a maiden, to advise a maiden
    To slight the jacket blue!"

6. "A tarry sailor I'll ne'er disdain,
    Always true till he comes again.
    So drink his health; here's a piece of coin.
    But my dark-eyed sailor, but my dark-eyed sailor
    Still claims this heart of mine."

7. When William did the ring unfold
    She seem'd distracted midst joy and woe.
    "You're welcome, William; I have lands and gold
    For my dark-eyed sailor, for my dark-eyed sailor,
    So manly, true and bold!"

8. Down in a cottage by a riverside,
    In peace and harmony they now reside.
    So, girls, prove true whilst your lover's away.
    Oft a cloudy morning, oft a cloudy morning
    Brings forth a pleasant day.

THE BAILIFF'S DAUGHTER OF ISLINGTON

Almost the same story is told as in "The Dark Eyed Sailor" but to a jaunty, bouncy melody.

STRUM: IA or IXA

ENGLAND

Arr. by N. L.

Moderately (♩=96)

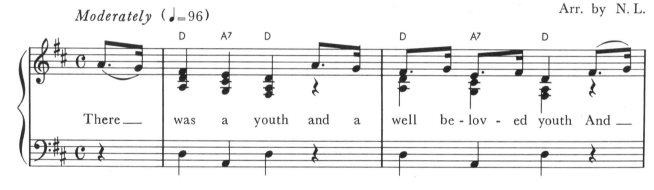

There ___ was a youth and a well be - lov - ed youth And ___

100

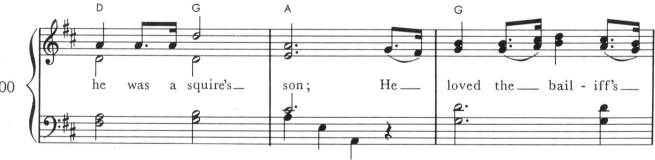

he was a squire's ___ son; He ___ loved the ___ bail - iff's ___

daugh - ter ___ dear, That lived ___ in ___ Is - ling - ton.

(♩) ♩ ♩ ♩ ♩ ♩ ♩ ♩

2. Yet   she   was   coy   and   would   not be-   lieve . . . .
That   he   did   love   her   so, ...
No,   nor   at   an — y   time   would   she . . . . .
An — y   coun-te — nance   to   him   show. . . . .

3. But   when   his   friends   did   un — der — stand . . . .
His   fond   and   fool — ish   mind, ...
They   sent   him   up   to   fair   Lon — don   town, . . .
An ap — pren — tice   for   to   bind. . . . .

4. And   when   he   had   been   sev — en   long   years, . . .
And   nev — er   his   love   could   see; . . . .
"Man-y a   tear   have   I   shed   for   her   sake . . . .
When   she   lit—tle   thought   of   me." . . . .

5. Then   all   the   maids   of   Is — ling — ton . . . . .
Went   forth   to   sport   and   play; . . . .
All   but   the   bail — iff's   daugh — ter   dear, ...
She   se-cret — ly   stole   a — way. . . . .

6. She   pull — éd   off   her   gown   of   green, . . .
And   put   on some   rag-ged   at — tire; . . . .
And   to   fair   Lon — don   she   would   go, ...
Her   true   love   to   en — quire. . . . .

7. And   as   she   went   a — long the   high   road, ...
The   weath-er   be — ing   hot   and   dry, ...
She   sat   her   down   up — on a   green   bank . . . .
And her   true   love came   rid — ing   by. . . . .

8. She   start — ed   up   with a   col — or   so   red, ...
Catch-ing   hold   of his   brid — le   rein; . . . .
"One   pen-ny,   one   pen-ny,   kind   sir,"   she   said, ...
"Will   ease   me   of   much   pain." . . . .

9. "Be — fore   I   give   you one   pen-ny   fair   maid, . . .
Pray   tell   me where   you   were   born." . . . .
"At   Is — ling — ton,   kind   sir,"   said   she, ...
"Where   I   have had   man — y a   scorn." . . . .

10. "If   that   be   so,   I   prith-ee,   fair   maid, . . .
Oh,   tell   me   wheth-er   you   know . . . .
The   bail — iff's   daugh — ter of   Is — ling — ton?" . . .
"She is   dead,   sir,   long   a — go." 101

11. "If   she   be   dead,   then   take   my   horse, . . .
My   sad-dle   and   brid-le   al — so; . . . .
For   I   will in — to   some   far   coun — try . . . . . .
Where   no   man   shall   me   know." . . . .

12. "Oh   stay,   oh   stay,   thou   good — ly   youth, . . .
She   stand — eth   by   thy   side; . . . .
She   is   here a — live,   she   is   not   dead, . . .
And   read — y   to   be   thy   bride." . . . .

13. "Oh,   fare — well   grief   and   wel — come   joy . . . . .
Ten   thous — and   times   there — fore; . . . .
For   now   I have   found   my   own   true   love, ...
Whom I   tho't I   nev — er   should   see   more." . . . .

VALIANT MARINE

An unhappy ending is the chief difference between the story told in this song and the two which preceded it.

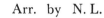

STRUM: I-C

FRANCE

Arr. by N. L.
Eng. version by W. S.

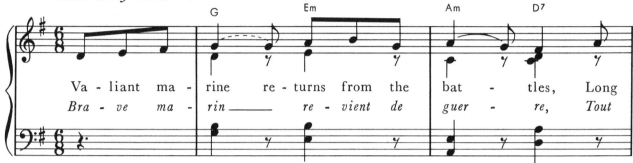

Moderately slow (♩.=72)

Va - liant ma - rine re - turns from the bat - tles, Long
Bra - ve ma - rin re - vient de guer - re, Tout

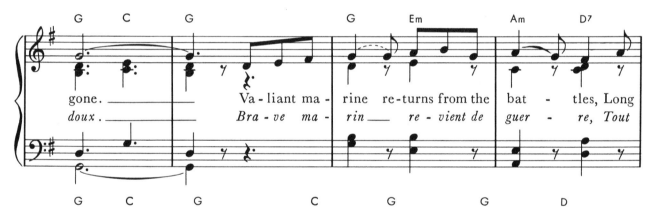

gone._____ Va - liant ma - rine re-turns from the bat - tles, Long
doux._____ Bra - ve ma - rin re - vient de guer - re, Tout

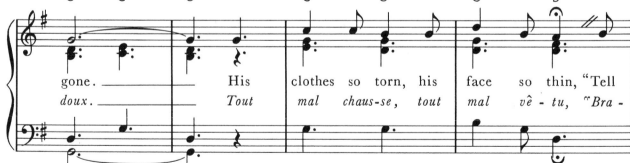

102

gone._____ His clothes so torn, his face so thin, "Tell
doux._____ Tout mal chaus-se, tout mal vê - tu, "Bra-

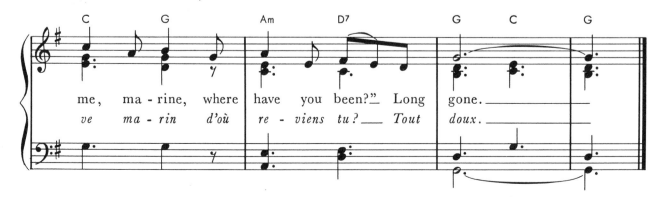

me, ma - rine, where have you been?" Long gone._____
ve ma - rin d'où re - viens tu?_____ Tout doux._____

2. "Lady, I've just returned from the battles." } twice
   Long gone.
   "Pray fetch for me a glass of wine,
   To satisfy this thirst of mine."
   Long gone.

3. Valiant marine, he drinks to his youthful days. } twice
   Long gone.
   He sings a song of earlier years,
   The lady soon gives way to tears.
   Long gone.

4. "Tell me, dear lady, what are you crying for?" } twice
   Long gone.
   "Do you begrudge this single glass
   That I have ask'd for as I pass?"
   Long gone.

5. "I don't begrudge the glassful of wine I give." } twice
   Long gone.
   "But when you sing my heart grows sore,
   Rememb'ring one I'll see no more."
   Long gone.

6. "What of these children playing around you?" } twice
   Long gone.
   "When your man left, you had but three,
   But now before me six I see."
   Long gone.

7. "One of his comrades wrote me a letter;" } twice
   Long gone.
   "Your man," he said, "in battle died."
   So I again became a bride."
   Long gone.

8. Valiant marine, he drank up his glass of wine. } twice
   Long gone.
   In silence from the house he strode,
   Rejoin'd his outfit down the road.
   Long gone.

2. *«Madame, je reviens de guerre;*
   Qu'on apporte ice du vin blanc,
   Que le marin boive en passant.»

3. *Brave marin se met à boire*
   Se met à boire et à chanter:
   Et la belle hôtesse à pleurer:

4. *«Ah! dites-moi, la belle hotesse,*
   Regrettez-vous votre vin blanc,
   Que le marin boit en passant?»

5. *«Ce n'est pas mon vin que je regrette,*
   Mais c'est la mort de mon mari:
   Monsieur, vous ressemblez à lui . . .»

6. *«Ah, dites-mois, la belle hôtesse,*
   Vous aviez de lui trois enfants:
   Vous en avez six à présent!»

7. *«On m'a écrit de ses nouvelles,*
   Qu'il était mort et enterré . .
   Et je me suis remariée.»

8. *Brave marin vida son verre,*
   Sans remercier, tout en pleurant,
   S'en retourne à son bâtiment.

POOR YOUNG GIRL
POOR YOUNG MAN

These are not
folk songs,
but delightful
music hall travesties
on the same theme.

STRUM: IX

UNITED STATES

Freely (♩ = 72)

Arr. by N. L.

104

(Poor Young Girl) There once was a poor young girl who left her coun—try home, And
(Poor Young Man) There once was a poor young man who left his coun—try home, And

came to the ci—ty to seek em—ploy—ment.— She had to leave her home be—cause the
came to the ci—ty to seek em—ploy—ment.— He prom—ised his dear Moth—er that he'd

wolf was at the door, And her fa—ther had fall—en down and hurt his knee.
lead the sim—ple life And al—ways shun the fa—tal curse of drink.

2. Just before she went away, her sweetheart, whose name was Jack,
   Said to her, "I fear you will not be true."
   So she had to promise him, before she got on the train,
   That every night at eight o'clock she would burst into tears.

3. She came to the city and was riding on a street-car,
   When a man got up and offered her his seat.
   She refused the offer with scorn because she saw that he wore a ring,
   And she didn't know but that he might be a married man.

4. Then up stepped the conductor and said, "I knew you would be true!"
   And tore off his false whiskers and it was Jack!
   And that night she got a letter saying that her father's knee was better,
   And an aunt had died and left her fifty-eight thousand dollars.

2. He came to the city and accepted employment in a quarry,
   And while there he made the acquaintance of some college men.
   He little guessed that they were demons, for they wore the best of clothes,
   But clothes do not always make the gentleman.

3. One night he went with his new-found friends to dine,
   And they tried to persuade him to take a drink.
   They tempted him and tempted him, but he refused and he refused,
   Till finally he took a glass of beer.

4. When he seen what he had done, he dashed the liquor to the floor,
   And staggered to the door with delirium tremens.
   While in the grip of liquor, he met a Salvation Army lassie,
   And cruelly he broke her tambourine.

5. All she said was "Heaven bless you!", and placed a mark upon his brow
   With a kick that she had learned before she was saved.
   So, kind friends, take my advice and shun the fatal curse of drink,
   And don't go around breaking people's tambourines.

I KNOW MY LOVE

A charming, fey, lonesome love song.

STRUM: II-B or V-B

IRELAND

Arr. by N. L.

Moderately, with movement ($\quarternote = 92$)

106

I know my love by his way of walkin', and I know my love by his way of talk-in', and I know my love dressed in a suit of blue, and if my love leaves me, what shall I do?___

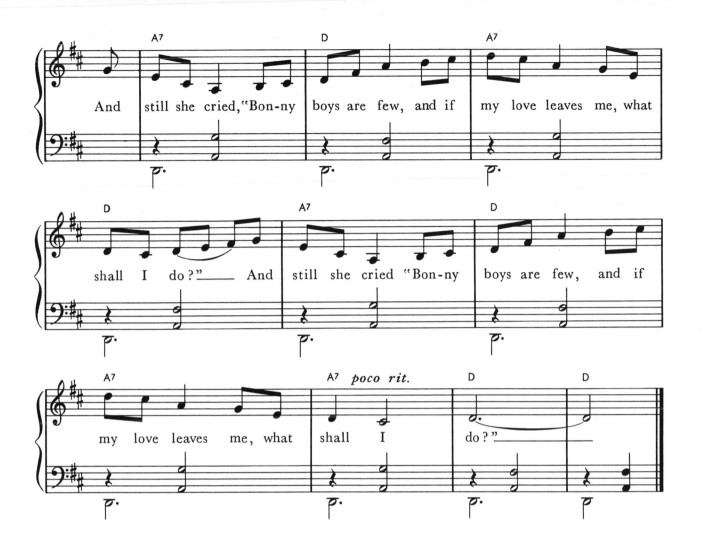

And still she cried, "Bon-ny boys are few, and if my love leaves me, what shall I do?" And still she cried "Bon-ny boys are few, and if my love leaves me, what shall I do?"

2. There is a dance house in Maradyke
   And there my true love goes every night.
   He takes a strange one upon his knee
   And don't you think now that vexes me!
   And still she cried, "I love him the best,
   And a troubled mind sure can know no rest."
   And still she cried, "Bonny boys are few,
   And if my love leaves me, what will I do?"

3. If my love knew I could wash and wring,
   If my love knew I could weave and spin,
   I'd make a coat all of the finest kind,
   But the want of money leaves me behind.
   And still she cried, "I love him the best,
   And a troubled mind sure can know no rest."
   And still she cried, "Bonny boys are few,
   And if my love leaves me, what will I do?"

107

THE WATER IS WIDE

Sometimes known as "O Waly, Waly," this is Scottish in origin
derived from "Jamie Douglas" and "Waly, Waly, up the Bank."

STRUM: VA

UNITED STATES
and
ENGLAND

Arr. by N. L.

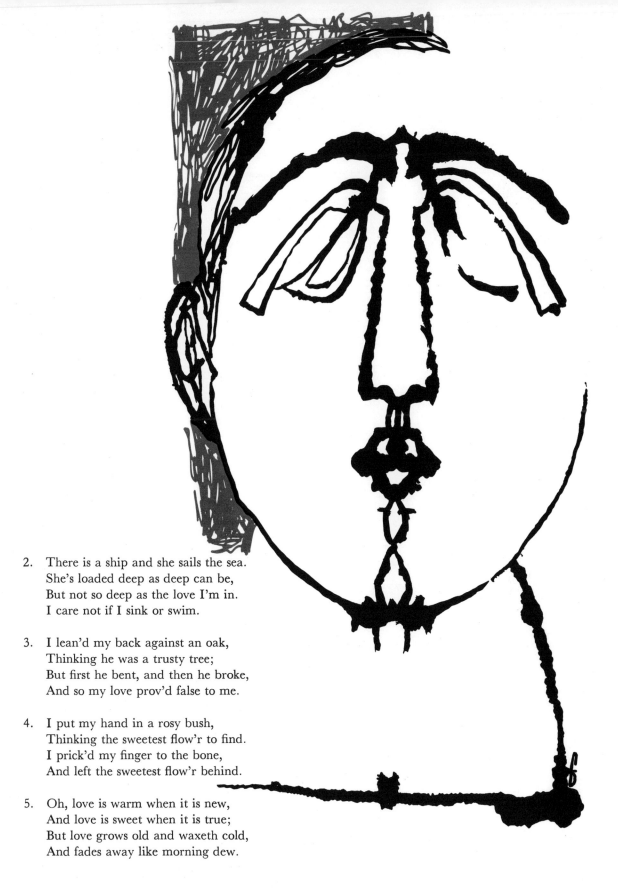

2. There is a ship and she sails the sea.
   She's loaded deep as deep can be,
   But not so deep as the love I'm in.
   I care not if I sink or swim.

3. I lean'd my back against an oak,
   Thinking he was a trusty tree;
   But first he bent, and then he broke,
   And so my love prov'd false to me.

4. I put my hand in a rosy bush,
   Thinking the sweetest flow'r to find.
   I prick'd my finger to the bone,
   And left the sweetest flow'r behind.

5. Oh, love is warm when it is new,
   And love is sweet when it is true;
   But love grows old and waxeth cold,
   And fades away like morning dew.

THE THREE HORSEMEN

Originating in the sixteenth century, this is a song of farewell to love, and resignation to death.

STRUM: Ic

GERMANY

Eng. Version by W. S.
Arr. by N. L.

Moderately (♩.=63)

Three horse-men are leav-ing by ear-ly dawn glow, A-
Es rit-ten drei Rei-ter zum Tho-re hin-aus. A-

way! ___ To join their bat-tal-lion on or-ders they go, A-
de! ___ Feins-lieb-chen schau-te zum Fen-ster her-aus, A-

way! ___ A girl from a win-dow, with man-ner so shy, calls
de! ___ Und wenn es denn soll ge-schie-den sein, so

soft-ly, "A glance to re-mem-ber you by." A-way! A-way! A-
reich' mir dein gol-de-nes Rin-ge-lein" A-de! A-de! A-

way! No-vem-ber must fol-low each May. ___
de! Ja, Schei-den und Mei-den thut weh! ___

110

2. The one who does part us is Death, I fear, Away!
   And many warm lips does he part every year. Away!
   He separates many a man from his wife
   Who might have lived happily all of his life.
   Away, *etc.*

3. He's parted the babe from the mother's embrace. Away!
   I wonder if ever I'll see your sweet face. Away!
   Then if not tomorrow (O, were it today),
   You'll see me or him come a-riding your way.
   Away, *etc.*

2. Und der uns scheidet, das ist der Tod, Ade!
   Er scheidet so manches Mündlein roth: Ade!
   Er scheidet so manchen Mann vom Weib,
   Die konnten sich machen viel Zeitvertreib.
   Ade, ade, ade!
   Ja, Scheiden und Meiden thut weh.

3. Er scheidet das Kindlein in der Wieg'n, Ade!
   Wann werd' ich mein schwarzbraunes Mädel doch krieg'n, Ade!
   Und ist es nicht morgen, ach, wär' es doch heut',
   Es macht' uns allbeiden gar grosse Freud'.
   Ade, ade, ade!
   Ja, Scheiden und Meiden thut weh.

HE'S GONE AWAY

The next three tunes of parting are sometimes known as "ten thousand mile songs." The first, a haunting Appalachian Mountain tune with a text which is a variant of "The Lass of Roch Royal."

STRUM: VIA, VA, or IIA

UNITED STATES

Moderately slow ($\quarternote = 80$)

Arr. by N. L.

Refrain
I'm goin' a-way for to stay a lit-tle while,___ ___ but I'm com-in' back, tho' I go ten thou-sand miles.___

Verse

1. And it's who will shoe your foot? And it's who will glove your hand? And it's
   And it's papa will shoe my foot, And it's mama will glove my hand, And it's

WINTER'S NIGHT

Note the similarities of the text to "He's Gone Away." The tune is of Scottish origin.

STRUM: V_B

UNITED STATES

Arr. by N. L.

As I rode out last win-ter's night, A - drink - in'—of sweet wine, Con-

ver - sin' with that pur-ty lit-tle girl That stole this heart of mine.

So fare you well, my own true love, So fare you— well for a while. I'm

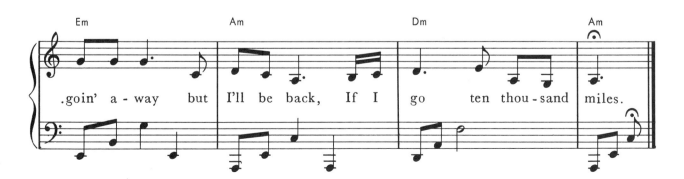

.goin' a - way but I'll be back, If I go ten thou-sand miles.

2. Oh, who will shoe your feet my love, ...
And who will glove your hand, ...
And who will kiss your red ros-y cheeks ......
While I'm gone to the for — eign land.

3. My fa-ther will shoe my feet, my love. ....
My moth — er will glove my hand, ...
And you will kiss my red ros-y cheeks ......
When you come from the for — eign land.

4. Oh, don't you see that lone — some dove ......
A — fly-in' from vine to vine, ...
A — mourn — in' for the loss of a mate, ...
And why not me for mine.

5. Yes, love, I see that lone — some dove ......
A — fly-in' from vine to vine, ...
A — mourn — in' for the loss of a mate, ...
Just like I am for mine.

115

MARY ANN

Another "song of parting," this forecastle shanty is Irish originally, out of French Canada.

STRUM: VIA or IIA

CANADA

Arr. by N. L.

Moderately slow (♩=80)

Then __ fare thee well my own true __ love, Then __ fare thee well for a
while, For the ship is a-wait-ing and the wind blows free, And
I am bound __ a way to the sea, Ma-ry Ann, And __
I am bound __ a way to the sea, Ma-ry Ann.

116

(♩)   ♩   ♩   ♩   ♩   ♩   ♩   ♩ (♩)

2. Oh, don't you see that pret — ty tur — tle dove, ...
    Sit — ting on a pine? . . . .
    He's mourn — ing the loss of his own true love, ...
    As I now mourn for mine, my dear, } *twice*
    Ma — ry Ann. . . . .

3. The lob — ster boil — ing in the pot, ...
    And the cray — fish on the line; . . . .
    They're suf — f'ring long, but it's noth — ing like . . . . .
    The ache I bear for you, my dear, } *twice*
    Ma — ry Ann. . . . .

4. Oh, had I but a bot — tle of gin, ...
    And su — gar here for two; . . . .
    And a great big bowl for to mix it in, ...
    I'd fix a drink for you, my dear, } *twice*
    Ma — ry Ann. . . . .
Repeat first verse.

COME ALL YE FAIR AND TENDER LADIES

A tale of duplicity and false love from the Southern mountains.

STRUM: IIA

UNITED STATES

Arr. by N. L.

Moderately (♩ = 60)

Come all ye fair and ten - der la - dies,

Take warn - in' how you court young men.

They're like a star on a sum - mer's morn - ing.

First they'll ap - pear and then they're gone.

2. They'll tell to you some loving story,
   And they'll declare their love is true.
   Straight way they'll go and court some other,
   And that's the love they have for you.

3. O, don't you remember our days of courtin',
   When your head lay upon my breast?
   You could make me believe by the falling of your arm,
   That the sun rose in the west.

119

4. If I had known before I courted,
   That love had been so hard to win;
   I'd have locked my heart in a box of golden,
   And fastened it up with a silver pin.

5. I wish I were a little sparrow,
   And I had wings, and I could fly;
   I'd fly away to my false true lover,
   And when he'd speak I would deny.

6. But I am not a little sparrow.
   I have no wings, nor can I fly.
   I will sit right down in grief and sorrow,
   And try to pass my troubles by.

THE SEEDS OF LOVE

There are many songs in which flowers or herbs represent the "false lover." This is a particularly beautiful example. When Cecil Sharp heard an uneducated English gardener sing "The Seeds of Love," he decided that, contrary to the belief of his contemporaries, there was a living English folk song tradition, and soon after embarked on the research in England and America which proved him to be correct.

STRUM: VA

ENGLAND

Arr. by N. L.

Moderately slow ($\quad$= 88)

I sowed the seeds of love, And I sowed them in the___ spring.___ I gath-ered them up___ in the morn-ing so soon, While the small birds so sweet-ly sing.___ While the small birds so sweet-ly sing.

(♩) ♩ ♩ ♩ ♩ ♩ ♩ ♩

2. My gar — den was plant — ed well . . . .
With flow — ers ev' — ry where, ...
But I had not the lib — er — ty to choose for my — self
Of the flow'rs that I loved so dear, ... *(repeat)*

3. The gard'n — er was stand — ing by, ...
And I asked him to choose for me. . . . .
He chose for me the vi — o — let, the li — ly and the pink,
But those I re — fused all three. . . . . *(repeat)*

4. The vi — o — let I did not like . . . .
Be — cause it bloomed so soon. . . . .
The li — ly and the pink I real — ly ov — er think,
So I vowed I would wait 'til June. . . . . *(repeat)*

5. In June there was a red rose — bud, ...
And that is the flow'r for me. . . . .
I oft — en — time have pluck'd that red rose — bud,
Till I gain'd the wil — low tree. . . . . *(repeat)*

6. The wil — low tree will twist, ...
And the wil — low tree will twine. . . . .
I oft — en — time have wished I were in that young man's arms
That once had the heart of mine. . . . . *(repeat)*

7. Come all you false young men. . . . .
Do not leave me here to com plain, ...
For the grass that has oft — en — time been tramp – led un — der foot,
Give it time. It will rise a — gain. . . . . *(repeat)*

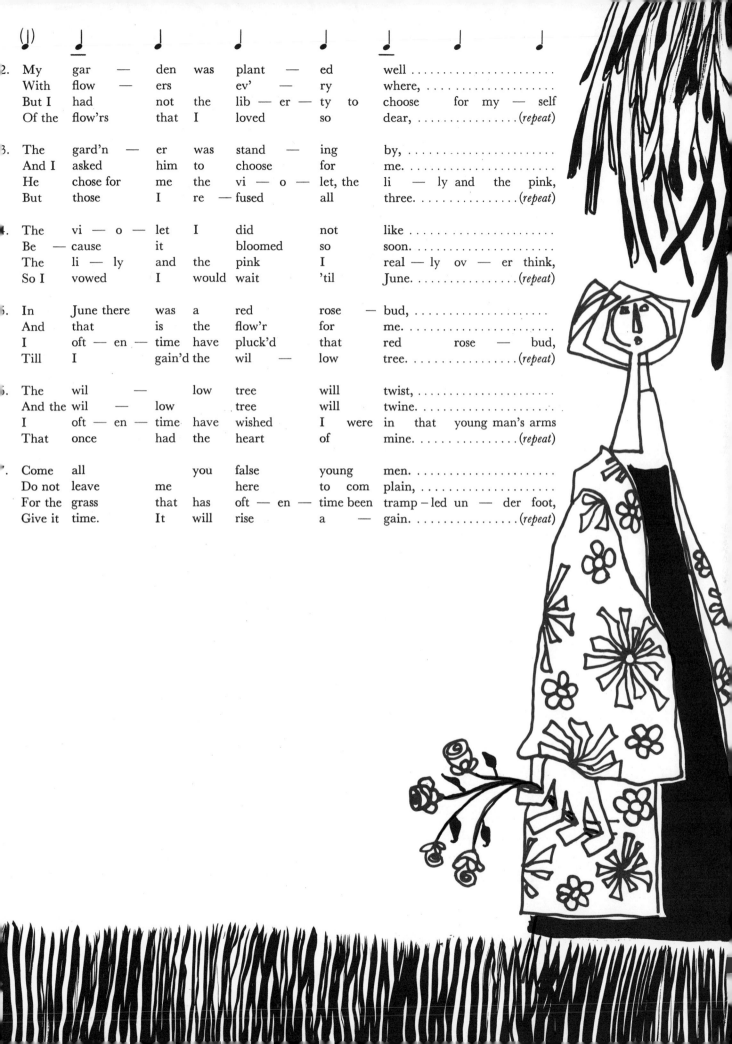

THE TREES THEY DO GROW HIGH

An unusual modal tune from Somerset. Here too, the rhythmic character of the tune belies the tragedy of the text.

STRUM: Ic

ENGLAND

With movement - Not too slow (♩.=96)

Arr. by N. L.

The trees they do grow high, and the leaves they do grow green, But the time is gone and past, my love,— that you and I have seen. It's a cold win - ter's night, my love, and here I must a - bide a - lone. My bon - ny lad was young, but a - grow-ing.____

122

2. "O,   Father, dearest Father, I fear you've done me wrong,
   For you've married me to a bonny boy, but I fear he is too young."
   "O, my daughter, dearest daughter, if you stay at home a time with me,
   A   lady you shall be, while he's growing?"

3. "We'll send him to a college for a year or two,
   And   then perhaps in time, my love, into a man he'll grow.
   I will buy you a ribbon blue to tie about his bonny waist,
   To   let the ladies know that he's married."

4.   At the age of sixteen, he was a married man,
   And   at the age of seventeen, he was father of a son,
   And   at the age of eighteen, his grave it was a growing green,
   And   that did put an end to his growing.

5. She   made her love a shroud of the holland, O so fine,
   And   ev'ry stitch she put in it, her tears came trinkling down.
   "O,   once I had a sweetheart, but now I have got never a one,
   So   fare you well my true love for ever."

6. "The   trees they do grow high and the leaves they do grow green,
   But the time is gone and past, my love, that you and I have seen.
   It's a cold winter's night, my love, and here I must abide alone.
   So   fare you well my true love, for ever."

THE WILLOW TREE

In the next three songs, the disappointed lover identifies with the drooping weeping willow as a symbol of unrequited love and self-pity.

STRUM: IIB

Slowly (♩ = 76)

Arr. by N. L.

O, take me to your arms, love, for keen doth the wind blow; O, take me to your arms, love, for bit - ter is my deep woe. She hears me not, she heeds me not, nor will she lis - ten to me, While here I lie a - lone to die be-neath the will - low tree

(♩) ♩ ♩ ♩ ♩ ♩ ♩ ♩ ♩ ♩ ♩

2. My   love hath wealth   and   beau — ty, rich suit — ors   at — tend her door.
   My   love   hath wealth and beau — ty; she slights   me because I am poor.
   The   rib — bon fair   that   bound her hair is   all   that is left   to   me,
   While here   I   lie a — lone   to   die   be — neath the wil—low tree.

3. I   once had gold   and   sil — ver,   I   thought them with — out   end.
   I   once   had gold and sil — ver,   I   thought   I   had a   true   friend.
   My   wealth is lost,   my   friend is false. My love   hath he stol—en from me,
   While here   I   lie a — lone   to   die   be — neath the wil—low tree.

BURY ME BENEATH THE WILLOW

Another beautiful ballad of false love from the Southern mountains.

STRUM: VIA or IIA

UNITED STATES

Arr. by N. L.

Simply (♩ = 80)

Verse

1. My heart is sad and I am lone-ly,
2. Our wed-ding was to be to-mor-row.

Think-ing of the one I love.
Oh, dear God, where can he be?

Still I hope some
Now he's prom-ised

day I'll see him,
to an-oth-er

When we reach that land a-bove.
And no long-er thinks of me.

126

Refrain

So bur - y me be - neath the wil - low;
'Neath the weep-ing wil-low tree; And when he knows where
I am sleep - ing, Then per-haps he'll weep for me.

3. He told me: "Dear, I love no other;"
And I thought his words were true.
Then a friend of mine confided:
"He has been untrue to you."
Refrain:

127

DOWN BY THE SALLEY GARDENS

This poem by W. B. Yeats, the renowned Irish poet, has been set to many tunes. This, "The Maids of Mourne Shore" is the best known. 'Salley' means willow.

STRUM: VIA or IIA

IRELAND

Words by W. B. Yeats
Arr. by N. L.

Moderately slow (♩=76)

1. Down___ by the Sal- ley___ gar - dens, my___ love and___ I did
2. In a field___ by the___ ri - ver, my___ love and___ I did

meet. She___ passed the___ Sal - ley___ gar - dens with___
stand, And___ on my lean - ing___ shoul - der, she___

lit - tle snow white feet. She bid me___ take love
laid___ her snow white hand. She bid me___ take love

ea - sy, as the leaves grow___ on___ the___ tree, But___
ea - sy, as the grass grows___ on___ the___ weirs, But___

I be-ing young and___ fool - ish, with___ her did not a - gree.
I was___ young and___ fool - ish, and___ now am full of tears.

THE CUCKOO

THE CUCKOO IS A PRETTY BIRD

Except for national language differences, the verses of this "cuckoo" are identical with those of its American cousin, which follows later.

STRUM: VIB or IIB

ENGLAND

Arr. by N.L.

Moderately slow (♩ = 92)

The cuck-oo is a pret-ty bird, she sings as she flies; She bring-eth good ti - dings, she tells us no lies. She suck - eth sweet flow - ers to keep her voice clear, And when she sings cuck - oo, the sum - mer draws near.

130

2. O   meeting is a pleasure
And   parting is grief;
A   false-hearted lover
Is   worse than a thief.
A   thief can but rob you
Of   all that you have,
But a   false-hearted lover
Will   bring you to the grave.

3. The   grave will receive you
And   turn you to dust.
A   false-hearted lover
No   poor maid can trust.
They'll court you, they'll kiss you,
In   all ways deceive;
There's not one in twenty
A   maid can believe.

4. Come   all you young fair maids
Where- ever you be;
Don't   hang your affections
On a   sycamore tree.
The   leaves they will wither,
The   roots will decay
A-   las, I'm forsaken
And   wasting away.

THE CUCKOO'S SPRING SONG

The cuckoo heralds
Spring, and Spring is
for lovers. So, lovers
love the cuckoo.

WALES

Eng. version by W.S.
Arr. by N.L.

STRUM: Ia

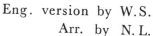

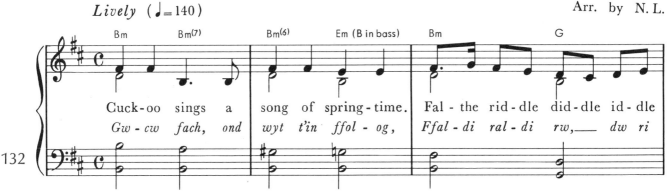

Lively (♩ = 140)

Cuck-oo sings a | song of spring-time. | Fal - the rid-dle did-dle id-dle
Gw - cw fach, ond | *wyt t'in ffol - og,* | *Ffal - di ral - di rw,___ dw ri*

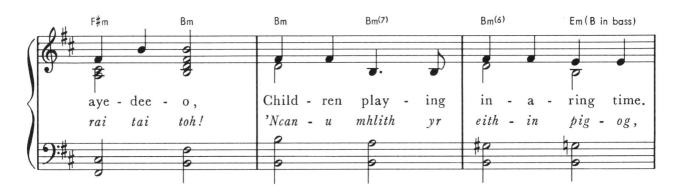

aye - dee - o, | Child - ren play - ing | in - a - ring time.
rai tai toh! | *'Ncan - u mhlith yr* | *eith - in pig - og,*

132

2. Lovers hand in hand do wander.
Fal the riddle diddle iddle aye dee O.
Hours in work they would not squander.
Fal the riddle diddle iddle aye dee O.
Cuckoo sings by day, by night-time.
Fal the riddle aye dee aye dee O.
Any hour for love's the right time.
Fal the riddle aye dee aye dee O.

3. On a bank, nearby the rushes,
Fal the riddle diddle iddle aye dee O.
Young man sighs and maiden blushes.
Fal the riddle diddle iddle aye dee O.
Cuckoos sing a song of mating.
Fal the riddle aye dee aye dee O.
May is here, we're celebrating.
Fal the riddle diddle iddle aye dee O.

133

SOFTLY CALLS THE CUCKOO

An heroic cuckoo, trumpeting a call to rise against oppression. This melody has been used by many Slavic composers, notably Bartok.

STRUM: IX

BULGARIA

Eng. version by W.S.
Arr. by N.L.

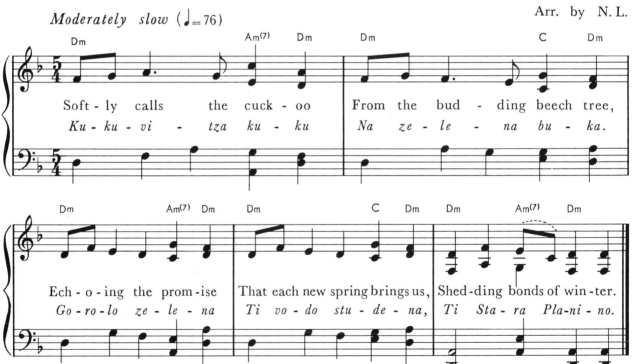

Moderately slow (♩ = 76)

Soft - ly calls the cuck - oo
Ku - ku - vi - tza ku - ku

From the bud - ding beech tree,
Na ze - le - na bu - ka.

Ech - o - ing the prom - ise
Go - ro - lo ze - le - na

That each new spring brings us,
Ti vo - do stu - de - na,

Shed - ding bonds of win - ter.
Ti Sta - ra Pla - ni - no.

134

2. Bravely calls the cuckoo
   To the scattered heroes:
   "Rise again and drive out
   Strangers from our lowlands.
   Hail our ancient glories."

3. Sadly calls the cuckoo
   In the mountain fastness,
   Mourning for the fallen;
   Asking of the living:
   "What became of freedom?"

2.
Voivitzi se pishat
I voinishko selo
Gorolo Zelena
Ti vodo studena
Ti stara planino.

THE CUCKOO

The verses are like the English cuckoo, and the tune is similar to the "Railroad Corral," a well-known trail-riding cowboy song.

STRUM: VB or IIB

Moderately fast and cheerfully (♩=112)

UNITED STATES
Arr. by N. L.

The— cuck-oo is a pret-ty bird, she sings as she flies. She— brings me good tid-ings and tells me no lies. She sips all the pret-ty flow-ers to make her voice clear, And she nev-er sings cuck-oo till the spring of the year.

135

2. A walkin' and talkin' from mornin' till night,
To walk with Sweet Willie, it was my delight.
If I am forsaken, I'll not be forsworn,
And he is mistaken, if he thinks I will mourn.

3. Come all you fair ladies, take a warnin' from me;
Don't place your affection on a green-growin' tree.
The leaves they will wither, the roots they will die.
If I am forsaken, I right well know why.
Repeat first verse

THE CUCKOO'S WELCOME

To the Swiss, the coming of Spring means the passing of the snows, the reawakening of the earth.
This tune has great possibilities for echo effects.

STRUM: IIC

SWITZERLAND

Eng. version by W.S.
Arr. by N.L.

Moderately fast (♩=100)

Verse

The snows of March have left us, The cold of A-pril, too,____ And
L'in- ver- no e pas- sa- to L'a- pri- le non c'e piu____ E

now in May we wel- come The bird that sings cuck- oo.____ Cuck-
ri- tor- na- to il mag- gio Al can- to del cu- cu.____ Cu-

Refrain

oo, cuck oo, To snow and cold a- dieu. We
cu, cu- cu, L'a- pri- le non c'e piu. E

sing a song to wel- come The bird that sings cuck- oo.____
ri- tor- na- to il mag- gio Al can- to del cu- cu.____

136

2. The calf now seeks its mother.
   The lamb doth seek the ewe;
   While up above doth hover
   The bird that sings cuckoo.
   Refrain

3. So listen all you maidens;
   When young men swear they're true—
   Just join the birds in singing
   The song that says "cuckoo."
   Refrain

137

SUMMER IS A-COMIN' IN

Dating back to the early thirteenth century, this is one of the first examples of the Round. It's attributed to John of Forsete, a monk of Reading Abbey.

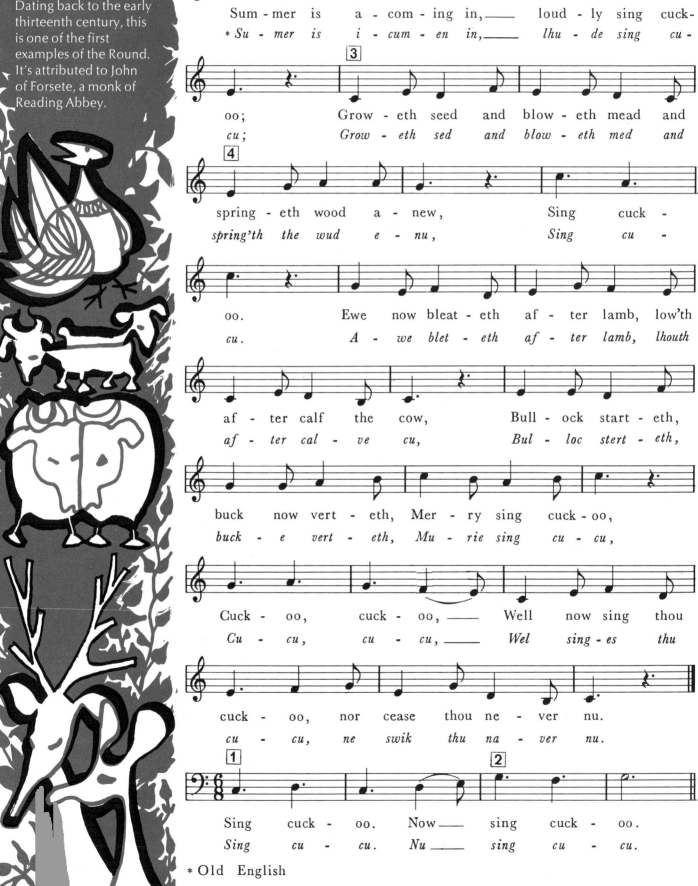

Moderately fast and cheerfully (♩.=104)

Sum - mer is a - com - ing in,____ loud - ly sing cuck-
*Su - mer is i - cum - en in,____ lhu - de sing cu -

oo; Grow - eth seed and blow - eth mead and
cu; Grow - eth sed and blow - eth med and

spring - eth wood a - new, Sing cuck -
spring'th the wud e - nu, Sing cu -

oo. Ewe now bleat - eth af - ter lamb, low'th
cu. A - we blet - eth af - ter lamb, lhouth

af - ter calf the cow, Bull - ock start - eth,
af - ter cal - ve cu, Bul - loc stert - eth,

buck now vert - eth, Mer - ry sing cuck - oo,
buck - e vert - eth, Mu - rie sing cu - cu,

Cuck - oo, cuck - oo, ____ Well now sing thou
Cu - cu, cu - cu, ____ Wel sing - es thu

cuck - oo, nor cease thou ne - ver nu.
cu - cu, ne swik thu na - ver nu.

Sing cuck - oo. Now____ sing cuck - oo.
Sing cu - cu. Nu____ sing cu - cu.

* Old English

LOOK MISTER CUCKOO

No intrigue, no deception. The Finnish cuckoo
is a happy, uncomplicated bird.

FINLAND
Eng. Version by W. S.
Arr. by N. L.

STRUM: VA or IA

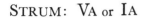

Lively and rhythmically (♩ = 69)

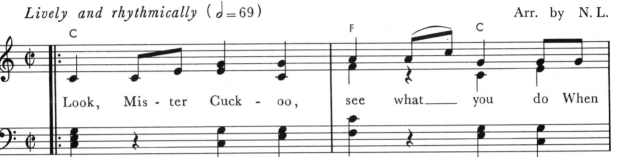

Look, Mis - ter Cuck - oo, see what___ you do When

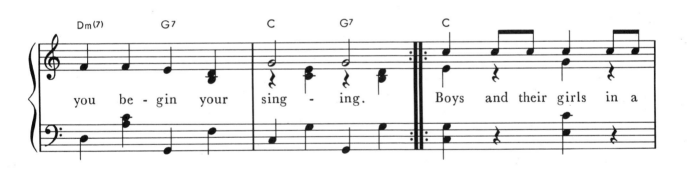

you be - gin your sing - ing. Boys and their girls in a

cir - cle danc - ing, With joy___ their___ hearts are ring - ing.

139

Oh, Mister Cuckoo, how we'll miss you } *twice*
When you leave in September;
But you have such a simple tune
That it's easy to remember. } *twice*

THE CUCKOO'S ADVICE

This time is very reminiscent of the mazurka, a swinging Polish dance.

STRUM: VIB or IIB

POLAND
Eng . Version by W. S.
Arr. by N. L.

Moderately fast (♩=108)

Verse

Lit - tle bird sings cuck - oo / to a mate who's / wait - ing. That's the
Ku - ku - lecz - ka ku - ka, / chlo - piec pan - ny / szu - ka, Spo - zie-

right thing to do / when it's time for / mat - ing.
ra prze - bie - ra, / i no - sa zad - zie - ra.

Refrain

Cuck - oo, / cuck - oo, / Come to me, / come to me;
Ku - ku, / ku - ku / a - a - cha, / a - a - cha,

If you don't, I'll / fly a - way and sing my / mel - o - dy un - to an - oth - er.
Lo - di ry - di / lo - di ry - di dy - na / lo - di ry - di dy - na a - cha.

140

2. As I walk thru the woods
   All my doubts assail me.
   My love's so hard to please.
   What if love's words fail me.
   Cuckoo, Cuckoo,
   Speak for me, speak for me.
   She's the only one I love, and if I lose her,
   I won't find another.

3. O, you stupid young man!
   If she should refuse you,
   There are others who can
   Hear your words and choose you.
   Cuckoo, Cuckoo,
   Come with me, come with me.
   If we cannot have the ones we long for,
   We shall surely find some others.

2. Chłopcy moje chłopcy
   W co wy to dufacie,
   Czy to w te surduty
   Co po jednym macie.
   Kuku, kuku,
   A-a-cha, a-a-cha,
   Lodi rydie, lodi rydie dyna
   Lodi rydi dina a-cha.

141

3. Poznać ci to poznać
   Chłopca fanfarona,
   Choc pusto w kieszeni
   Głowa naiżona.
   Kuku, kuku, *etc.*

The melody is early nineteenth century;
the words, around 1835. (From the
singing of Anna Rodenburg Stracke)

THE LOVER'S CUCKOO

STRUM: VIB or IIB

GERMANY
Eng. Version by W. S.
Arr. by N. L.

Moderately fast, gaily (♩ = 160)

| E | E | B7 | E |

Cuck - oo,   Cuck - oo,   sings   thru   the   trees.
Kuck - uk,   *Kuck - uk,*   *ruft*   *aus*   *dem*   *Wald.*

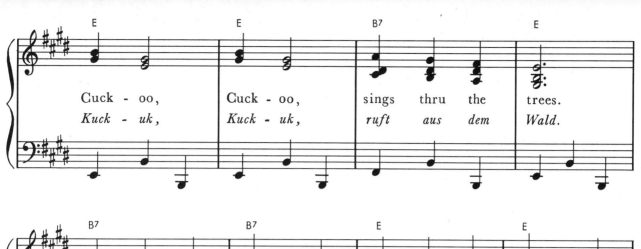

Cuck - oo, Cuck - oo, sings thru the trees.
Kuck - uk, *Kuck - uk,* *ruft aus dem Wald.*

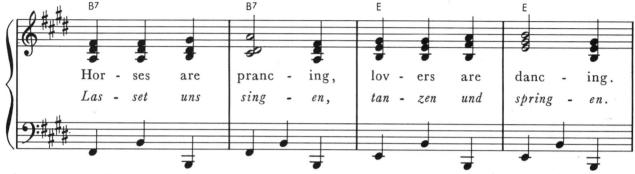

Hor - ses are pranc - ing, lov - ers are danc - ing.
Las - set uns sing - en, *tan - zen und spring - en.*

Cuck - oo, Cuck - oo, give my heart ease.
Früh - ling *Früh - ling,* *wird es nun bald.*

2. Cuckoo, cuckoo, winter is past.
   Cuckoo, cuckoo, winter is past.
   Farmers all plowing, lovers all vowing,
   Cuckoo, cuckoo, spring's here at last.

3. Cuckoo, cuckoo, tell her it's spring, *(twice)*
   My heart is burning; for love I'm yearning.
   Cuckoo, cuckoo, I, too, would sing.

2. Kuckuk, Kuckuk, lässt nicht sein Schrei'n,
   Kuckuk, Kuckuk, lässt nicht sein Schrei'n,
   Komm' in die Felder, Weisen und Wälder!
   Frühling, Frühling, stelle dich ein!

3. Kuckuk, Kuckuk, trefflicher Held! *(twice)*
   Was du gesungen, ist dir gelungen!
   Winter, Winter, räumet das Feld.

143

AS I ME WALKÉD AS I
AS I ME WALKÉD AS
AS I ME WALKÉD
AS I ME WALK

An early seventeenth century Round.

ENGLAND

Four part round

♩ = 56

As I me walk - éd in a May ___ morn -
ing, I heard a bird sing, "Cuck - oo".

BLUES AND COMPLAINTS

145

I'M A STRANGER HERE

A Negro blues. "Ain't it hard to stumble when you got no place to fall" is
one of the most descriptive lines in all the Blues literature.

STRUM: XI or IA

UNITED STATES

Arr. by N. L.

Moderately slow blues (♩ = 112)

Verse

Ain't it hard to stum-ble When you got no place to fall?
Ain't it hard to trav-el When you got no place to go?

Ain't it hard to stum-ble When you got no place to fall?
Ain't it hard to trav-el When you got no place to go?

146

In this whole wide world,___ I got no place at all.
Left my friends be-hind,___ there's no-one here I know.

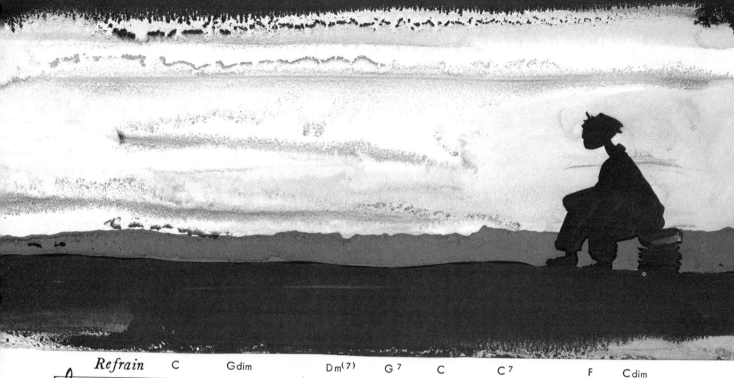

Refrain · C · Gdim · Dm(7) · G7 · C · C7 · F · Cdim

I'm a stran - ger here, _____ a stran-ger ev-ry-where, _____ I

C · Em(7) · A · Fm · G7 · Ab7 · G7 · C · F7 · C

could go home, but hon - ey, I'm a stran - ger there. _____

3. Went to sleep last night, in a snow white feather bed (*twice*)
I woke up this morn-ing with the blues all 'round my head.
Refrain

147

4. Looked down that road, just as far as I could see, (*twice*)
And a little bitty hand kept a-wavin' back at me.
Refrain

5. 'Druther be by a riv-er, sittin' on a hollow log (*twice*)
Than to have my ba-by treat me like a dirty dog.
Refrain

6. When you get you a wom-an, man, you better get you two (*twice*)
'Cause you just can't tell, what a woman's goin' to do.
Refrain

NINE HUNDRED MILES

This country blues song, Negro in origin, is related to the bitter "Reuben Blues."
The railroad whistle is so often found in folklore as a symbol of loneliness.

STRUM: IVA or IA

UNITED STATES

Lively ($\quarternote = 108$)

Arr. by N. L.

I'm a walk-in' down the track, I've got tears in my eyes,

Tryin' to read a let-ter from my home._____ If this

train_____runs me right, I'll be home to-mor-row night, For I'm

nine hun - dred miles___ from my home,_____ And I

hate to hear that lone - some whis - tle blow.___

Refrain

I'll pawn you my watch, I'll___ pawn you my chain. I'll

D.S. al Fine

pawn you my gold___ dia - mond ring._____ If this

2. Oh, this train I ride on is a hundred coaches long.
   You can hear the whistle blow for many a mile.
   If this train runs me right,
   I'll be home tomorrow night,
   For I'm nine hundred miles from my home,
   And I hate to hear that lonesome whistle blow.
   Refrain

DELIA'S GONE

It's a long way from the Bahamas, but this is the old story of "Frankie and Johnny" transplanted.

STRUM: XI or IA

BAHAMAS

Arr. by N. L.

Moderately slow, with marked rhythm ($\quad$ = 108)

To-ny shot his De-lia, 'twas on a Fri-day night.

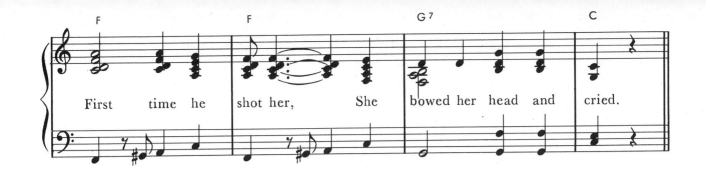

First time he shot her, She bowed her head and cried.

Refrain

De-lia's gone, one more round, De-lia's gone, (One more round,) De-lia's

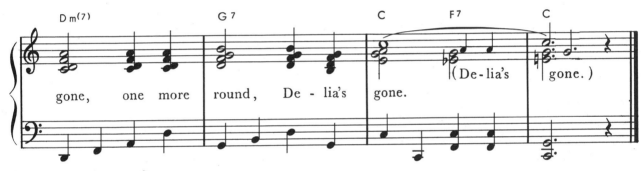

gone, one more round, De-lia's gone. (De-lia's gone.)

2.   Send for the doctor,
The   doctor came too late.
Send for the minister,
Poor Delia's met her fate.
Refrain

3.   Lord, they took my Delia,
They dressed her all in brown.
They took her to the graveyard;
I   saw them let her down.
Refrain

4.   Delia, Oh, Delia,
Oh, where you been so long?
All the people talkin' 'bout
My Delia's dead and gone.
Refrain

5.   Rubber tired carriage,
Rubber tired hack,
They took my Delia to the graveyard,
Ain't never gonna bring her back.
Refrain

151

THE COLORADO TRAIL

A beautiful cowboy song, Irish in origin. It's not usually considered a blues song, but if loneliness and longing are the requirements, then this fits by any standard.

STRUM: II-A

UNITED STATES

Arr. by N. L.

Moderately (♩ = 92)

Eyes like the morn-ing star, cheeks like a rose.

Lau - ra was a pret-ty girl, God al -migh-ty knows.

Weep, all ye lit - tle rains, Wail, winds,—— wail.

All a - long a - long, a-long the Co - lo - ra - do trail.

2. Stars fad—ing up a — bove, lark starts to sing, ...
    Sky is ros—y in the east, what will this day bring? . . . .
    Weep all ye lit — tle rains. Wail, winds, wail, ...
    All a—long, a—long, a—long, the Col — o—ra — do trail. . . . .

3. Eyes like a prai—rie flow'r, laugh—ing all the day, ...
    Lau—ra was a love—ly girl; now she's gone a — way. . . . .
    Weep all ye lit — tle rains. Wail, winds, wail, ...
    All a—long, a—long, a—long, the Col — o—ra — do trail. . . . .

POOR LONESOME COWBOY

Sentimental and maudlin is this lament. What could be bluer than the cry: "No father and no mother to take good care of me."

STRUM: IX

UNITED STATES

Arr. by N. L.

Slowly and mournfully - in a rubato style (♩ = 76)

Refrain

Chorus I'm a poor, lone-some cow-boy, I'm a poor, lone-some cow-boy, I'm a poor, lone-some cow-boy, and a long way from home.

Verse

1. I ain't got no fa-ther, I ain't got no moth-er, No fa-ther and no moth-er to take good care of me.
2. I ain't got no sis-ter, I ain't got no broth-er, No sis-ter and no broth-er to ride the range with me.

153

POOR OLD HORSE

Humans are not
the only creatures
who are maudlin.
Here is a case
of "equine self-pity."

STRUM: Ia

ENGLAND

Arr. by N. L.

Moderately (♩ = 184)

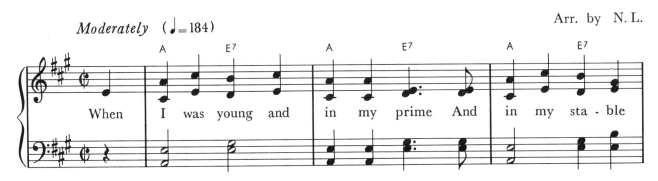

When I was young and in my prime And in my sta-ble

154

lay, They gave to me the ver-y best corn___ And the choic-est

hay. Poor old horse! Poor old mare!___

(♪)   ♩   ♩   ♩   ♩   ♩   ♩   ♩   (♪)

2. My   mas — ter   used   to   ride   me   out. . . . . . .
    And   tie   me   to   a   stile, ...
  And   he   was   court — ing   the   mil — ler's   girl,
  While   I   could   trot   a   mile.   Poor   old, *etc.*

3. Now   I   am   old   and   done   for, ...
    Fit   for   nothing   at   all. . . . .
  I'm   forced   to   eat   the   sour   grass
  That   grows   a —   gainst   the   wall.   Poor   old, *etc.*

4. Then   lay   my   tot — ter — ing   legs   so   low . . . .
    That   have   run   ve — ry   far, ...
  O'er   hedg — es   and   o'er   ditch — es,
  O'er   turn — pike   gate   and   bar.   Poor   old, *etc.*

5. My   hide   I'll   give   to the   hunts — man. . . . .
    My   shoes   I'll   throw   a — way. . . . .
  The   dogs   shall   eat   my   rot — ten   flesh,
  And   that's   how   I'll   de — cay.   Poor   old, *etc.*

SINGLE GIRL

It may be lonely being single, but the trials and tribulations are fewer.

STRUM: XI

Freely (♩ = 64)

Verse

UNITED STATES

ARR. BY N. L.

When I was sin-gle, I went dress'd so fine,

Now I am mar-ried, Lord, go rag-ged all the time.

STRUM: XI or I

Refrain (in strict tempo)

Lord, I wish I was a sin-gle girl a-gain.

Lord, I wish I was a sin-gle girl a-gain.

2. Dishes to wash,
   The spring to go to.
   When you are married, Lord,
   You got it all to do.
   Refrain:

3. I've three little children,
   All lyin' in bed,
   One of them so hungry
   He can't raise up his head.
   Refrain:

4. I wash their little feet,
   And send them to school.
   'Long comes that drunkard,
   And calls them a fool.
   Refrain:

5. When I was single,
   Ate biscuits and pie.
   Now I am married, Lord,
   It's eat cornbread or die.
   Refrain:

6. When I was single
   Marrying was my crave.
   Now I am married, Lord,
   Go troubled to my grave.
   Refrain:

157

MOLLY BRANNIGAN

Self-pitying as the lonesome cowboy and the
lonesome horse, but with an Irish brogue.

STRUM: IX

IRELAND

Freely (♩ = 96)

Arr. by N. L.

Mam, dear, and did you hear of pret-ty Mol-ly Bran-ni-gan? In
troth, dear, I have lost her, and I'll nev-er be a man a-gain; Not a
spot up-on me hide would an-oth-er sum-mer tan a-gain, Since
Mol-ly, she has left me all a-lone for to die. The

158

place where me heart was y'might eas-y roll a tur-nip in, As big as an-y pav-ing stone, from Dub-lin to the Dev-il's Glen; If she chose to take an-oth-er, sure she might have sent mine back a-gain, And not to leave me here ___ all a-lone for to die.

2.
	Mam, dear, I re — mem—ber	when the	milk—ing	time	was	past	and	done,
We	went in — to the	mea — dows	where she	swore I	was	the	on — ly	one
That	ev — er	she could	love,	yet	oh,	the	base,	the	cru — el	one,
	Af — ter	that to	leave me	all	a — lone	for	to	die.............
	Mam, dear, I re — mem—ber	as we	came home	the	rain	be — gan.
I	rolled her	in my	coat	tho	ne'er a	waist—coat I	had on.
My	shirt was	ra—ther	fine drawn, yet	oh,	the	base,	the	cru — el	one,
	Af — ter	that to	leave me	all	a — lone	for	to	die..............

3.
The	left	side	of my	car — cass	is	as	weak	as	wa — ter	gru — el,	Mam.
The	devil—a—bit	up — on	my	hide, since	Mol — ly's	been	so	cru — el,	Mam.
I	wish I	had a	blun — der — buss, I'd	go	and	fight	a	du — el,	Mam.
It's	bet — ter	far to	kill	my — self	than stay	here	to	die.............
I'm	cool	and de — ter — mined	as a	live	sa — la — man — der,	Mam;
Won't	you	come to my	wake	when I	go	my	long	me — an — der,	Mam?
I'll be	feel — ing	just as	val — iant	as the	fa — mous A — lex — an — der,	Mam,
When I	hear	you	cry—ing	'round me	"Arrah,	why	did	he die?"..............

WANDERIN'

This text has been widely sung to many tunes. It's probably only about forty-five years old, born out of the economic dislocation immediately following World War I.

STRUM: XI or IA

UNITED STATES

Arr. by N.L.

Slowly (♩=63)

My dad-dy is an en-gi-neer,___ My bro-ther drives a hack, My sis-ter takes in wash-ing,___ And the ba-by balls the jack, And it looks like___ I'm nev-er gon-na cease___ my wan - der - in'.

2. Oh, I've been awanderin' early and late,
From New York City to the Golden Gate;
Refrain:

3. Been workin' in the army, workin' on a farm,
And all I've got to show for it is muscle in my arm;
Refrain:

4. There's fish in the ocean, eels in the sea,
And a redheaded woman made a wreck of me;
Refrain:

160

FOR THE SMALL FRY

161

DANCE TO YOUR DADDY

A plaintive little tune for such a playful text.

STRUM: IIIB or IIB

ENGLAND

Arr. by N. L.

162

TANZ FRAYLACH

One can picture the child, too young to walk, being held up by the proud parent
saying: "That's the way to dance."

STRUM: Ib

EUROPE and U.S.

Eng. Version
and
Arr. by N.L.

Moderately (♩=120)

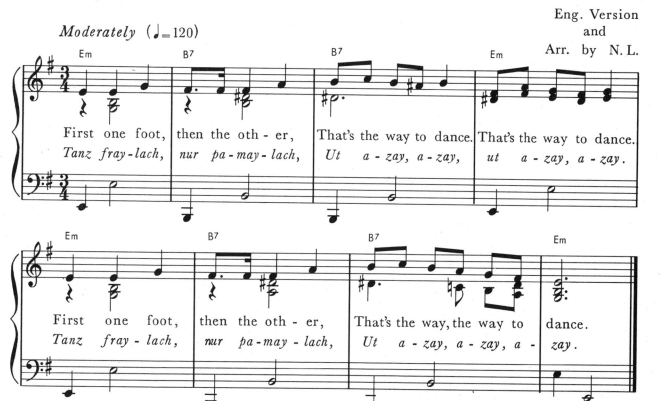

First one foot, then the oth - er, That's the way to dance. That's the way to dance.
Tanz fray-lach, nur pa-may-lach, Ut a - zay, a-zay, ut a - zay, a-zay.

First one foot, then the oth - er, That's the way, the way to dance.
Tanz fray - lach, nur pa-may - lach, Ut a - zay, a-zay, a - zay.

163

I LOVE MY ROOSTER

The tune may be the "Campbells are
Coming," but you've "got to crow."
It's a cumulative song.

STRUM: IIIB or IIB

UNITED STATES

Arr. by N. L.

Moderately fast (♩ = 176)

1. I love my roost-er, my roost-er loves me; I
2. I love my hen, my hen loves me; I

feed my roost-er on a cot-ton-wood tree, My
feed my hen on a cot-ton-wood tree, My

Go to ⊕ for all verses except verse 1

lit-tle old roost-er goes cock-a-dee-doo, Dee-

doo-dle dee, doo-dle dee, doo-dle dee doo.

D.C. al ⊕

164

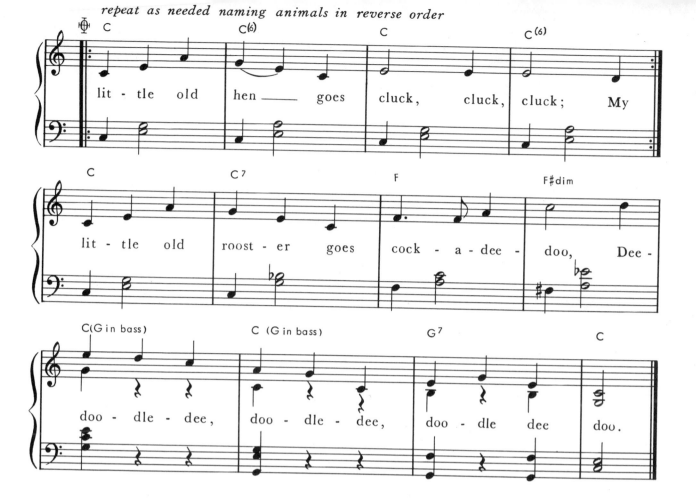

repeat as needed naming animals in reverse order

lit - tle old hen ——— goes cluck, cluck, cluck; My

lit - tle old roost - er goes cock - a - dee - doo, Dee -

doo - dle - dee, doo - dle - dee, doo - dle dee doo.

3. I love my pig, my pig loves me,
   I feed my pig on a cottonwood tree.
   My little old pig goes oink, oink, oink;
   My little old hen goes cluck, cluck, cluck;
   My little old rooster goes cockadee, doo dee,
   Doodledee, doodledee, doodledee, doo.

4. I love my cow, my cow loves me,
   I feed my cow on a cottonwood tree.
   My little old cow goes moo, moo, moo;
   Repeat pig, hen, rooster.

5. I love my horse, my horse loves me,
   I feed my horse on a cottonwood tree.
   My little old horse goes neigh, neigh, neigh;
   Repeat cow, pig, hen, rooster.

6. I love my dog, my dog loves me,
   I feed my dog on a cottonwood tree.
   My little old dog goes woof, woof, woof;
   Repeat horse, cow, pig, hen, rooster.

7. I love my cat, my cat loves me,
   I feed my cat on a cottonwood tree.
   My little old cat goes mew, mew, mew;
   Repeat dog, horse, cow, pig, hen, rooster.

8. I love my mouse, my mouse loves me,
   I feed my mouse on a cottonwood tree.
   My little old mouse goes eee, eee, eee;
   Repeat cat, dog, horse, cow, pig, hen, rooster.

9. I love my baby, my baby loves me,
   I feed my baby on a cottonwood tree.
   My little old baby goes waa, waa, waa;
   Repeat mouse, cat, dog, horse, cow, pig, hen, rooster.

165

LITTLE BIRD AT MY WINDOW

Birds, animals, and critters of all sorts play a large role in children's songs. This is a polite little "Vöglein."

STRUM: VIB or IIB

GERMANY
Eng. Version by W. S.
Arr. by N. L.

Moderately ($\quad = 104$)

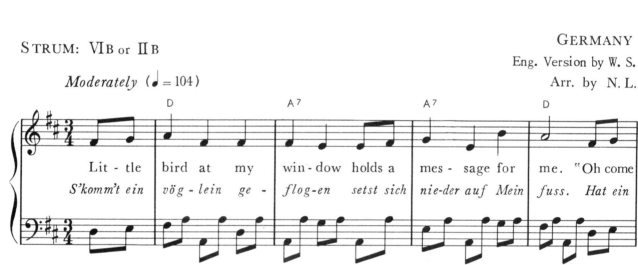

Lit - tle bird at my win - dow holds a mes - sage for me. "Oh come
S'komm't ein vög - lein ge - flog-en setst sich nie-der auf Mein fuss. Hat ein

166

to me, be - lov - ed, I am wait - ing for thee."
ze - tel im Scha - bel Bring-et freund - lich - en gruss.

2. Little bird, take this answer right back to my beau:
   "I would like to come to you, but my mama says 'no'."

3. Little birds sing a gay song, as they fly up above.
   "Oh, we're glad we're not people, when it's time to make love."

KUM BACHUR ATZEL

There's no nonsense about this Israeli rooster. He's an alarm clock and pet, all in one in this Round.

STRUM: IA

ISRAEL

Eng. Version and Arr. by N. L.

Vigorously (♩ = 112)

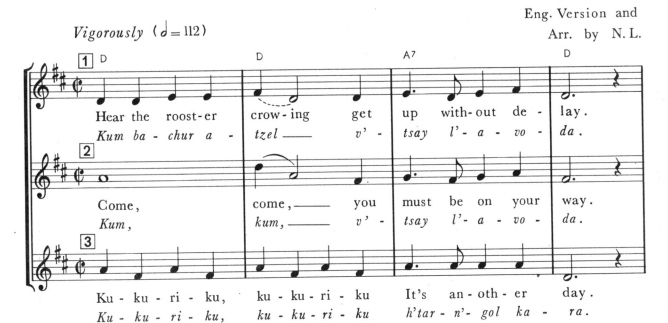

1 D — D — A7 — D

Hear the roost-er crow-ing get up with-out de - lay.
Kum ba - chur a - tzel ___ v' - tsay l'- a - vo - da.

2

Come, come, ___ you must be on your way.
Kum, kum, ___ v' - tsay l'- a - vo - da.

3

Ku - ku - ri - ku, ku - ku - ri - ku It's an - oth - er day.
Ku - ku - ri - ku, ku - ku - ri - ku h'tar - n'- gol ka - ra.

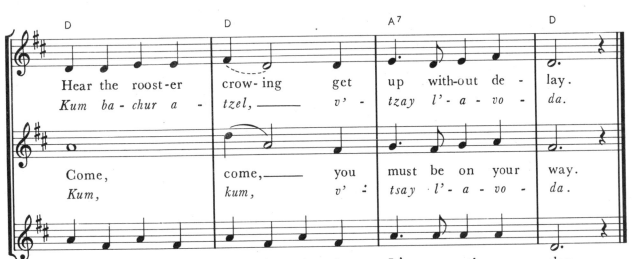

D — D — A7 — D

Hear the roost-er crow-ing get up with-out de - lay.
Kum ba - chur a - tzel, ___ v' - tzay l'- a - vo - da.

Come, come, ___ you must be on your way.
Kum, kum, v' - tsay l'- a - vo - da.

Ku - ku - ri - ku, ku - ku - ri - ku It's an - oth - er day.
Ku - ku - ri - ku, ku - ku - ri - ku h'tar - n'- gol - ka - ra.

167

MY PIGEON HOUSE

This tune, "Muss I Denn," has been everything from folk ballad to "hit" popular song. This version is an "activity" song.

STRUM: VIA or IIA

UNITED STATES

Moderately (♩ = 84)

Arr. by N. L.

My — pig-eon—house, I — o-pen—wide and I set my pig-eons

free. They— fly up,—high up — to the —sky, and they

sit on the high-est tree, And when they re-turn from their

mer-ry mer-ry flight, they shut their eyes and they say good night. Coo-

roo, coo-roo, coo —roo, coo-roo, coo — roo, coo-roo, coo — roo.

168

MY DAME HATH A LAME TAME CRANE

A tongue-twisting Round.

Lively (♩ = 60)

My dame hath a lame, tame crane. My dame hath a crane that is lame.

Pray, gen-tle Jane, let my dame's lame, tame crane feed and come home a - gain.

169

Preacher and congregation songs are common in spirituals. Here are Bible stories done "question and answer" style on the young-folk level.

WHO DID?

STRUM: IA

UNITED STATES

Arr. by N. L.

Fast (♩ = 116)

(Chorus) Who did, who did, who did, who did, Who did swal - low Jo - Jo - Jo - nah?

Who did, who did, who did, who did, Who did swal - low Jo - Jo - Jo - nah?

Who did, who did, who did, who did, Who did swal - low Jo - Jo - Jo - nah?

170

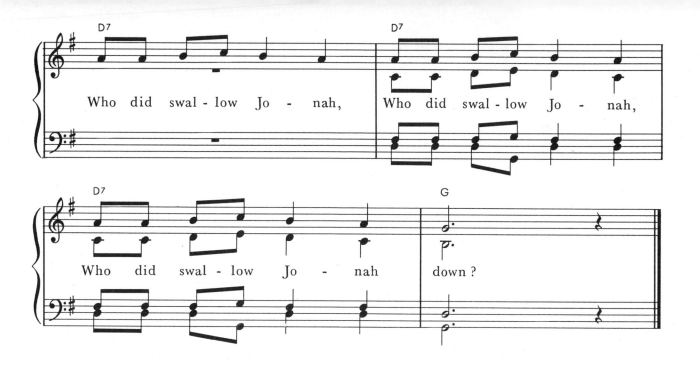

Who did swal-low Jo - nah,   Who did swal-low Jo - nah,

Who did swal-low Jo - nah   down?

2. Whale did, whale did, whale did, whale did,
   Whale did swallow Jo-Jo-Jonah.   } three times
   Whale did swallow Jonah,
   Whale did swallow Jonah,
   Whale did swallow Jonah up.

3. Daniel, Daniel, Daniel, Daniel,
   Daniel in the li-li-lion's,   } three times
   Daniel in the lion's,
   Daniel in the lion's,
   Daniel in the lion's den.

4. Gabriel, Gabriel, Gabriel, Gabriel,
   Gabriel blow your trum-trum-trum-pet,   } three times
   Gabriel blow your trumpet,
   Gabriel blow your trumpet,
   Gabriel blow your trumpet loud.

WHO BUILT THE ARK?

Here are the animals, two by two. This is also a dialogue between solo and group.

STRUM: Ia

Moderately fast ($\downarrow = 69$)

UNITED STATES
Add. Verses by W. S.
Arr. by N. L.

Refrain

Chorus: Who built the ark? No-ah! No-ah! Who built the ark? Broth-er

No-ah built the ark. Who built the ark? No-ah! No-ah!

Fine   *Verse*

172

Who built the ark? Broth-er No-ah built the ark. Old man No-ah

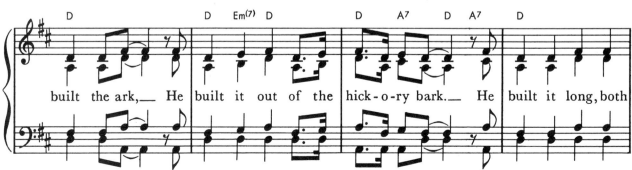

built the ark,__ He built it out of the hick-o-ry bark.__ He built it long, both

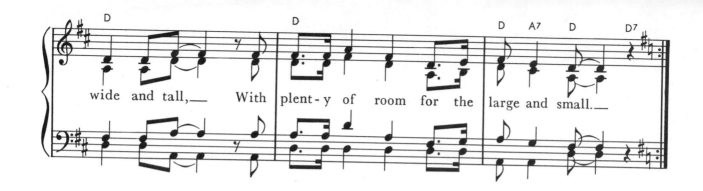

wide and tall,___ With plent-y of room for the large and small.___

2. He got him an axe and a hammer, too,
   Began to cut and began to hew.
   Ev'ry time that hammer ring,
   Old man Noah shouted and began to sing.
   Refrain

3. In come the animals, one by one.
   Little dog said, "I'm gonna have fun."
   In come the animals, two by two;
   Hippopotamus and kangaroo.
   Refrain

4. In come the animals, three by three;
   Two big cats and a bumble bee.
   In come the animals, four by four.
   Horse shouted out, "There's room for more."
   Refrain

5. In come the animals, five by five;
   Four little sparrows and a red bird's wife.
   In come the animals, six by six.
   Elephant laughed at the monkey's tricks.
   Refrain

6. In come the animals, seven by seven;
   Duck and her little ones, nine, ten, eleven.
   In come the animals, eight by eight;
   Cotton tailed rabbit and her mate.
   Refrain

7. In come the animals, nine by nine.
   Cow was laughin' and the bull was cryin'.
   In come the animals, ten by ten;
   Five black roosters and five white hens.
   Refrain

8. Noah said, "Go shut the door.
   The rain's started fallin' and we can't take more."
   Lightning flashed and thunder rolled.
   The animals were safe within the hold.
   Refrain

THE CRAWDAD SONG

A little nonsense, a little realism. Set to a high-spirited tune. When adults sing this song, the same words have quite different meanings.

STRUM: IA

UNITED STATES

Moderately (♩ = 92)

Arr. by N. L.

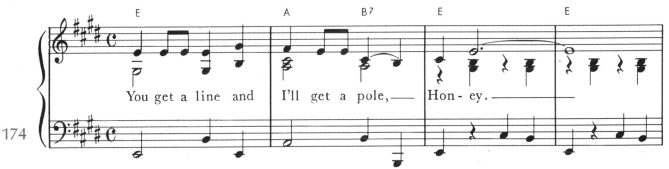

You get a line and I'll get a pole,— Hon - ey.—

174

You get a line and I'll get a pole,— Babe.—

You get a line and | I'll get a pole, | We'll go down to the | craw-dad hole,

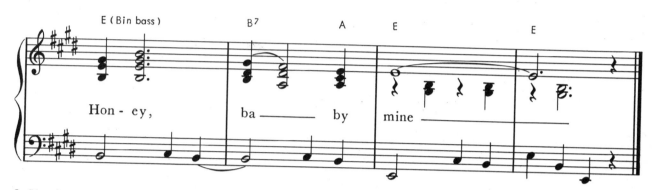

Hon - ey, | ba —— by | mine ——————— |

2. Yonder comes a man with a sack on his back, honey.
Yonder comes a man with a sack on his back, babe.
Yonder comes a man with a sack on his back,
Got more crawdads than he can pack,
Honey, baby mine.

3. What did the hen duck say to the drake, honey?
What did the hen duck say to the drake, babe?
What did the hen duck say to the drake?
Ain't no crawdads in this lake,
Honey, baby mine.

4. Sittin' on the bank 'til my feet got cold, honey.
Sittin' on the bank 'til my feet got cold, babe.
Sittin' on the bank 'til my feet got cold,
Watchin' that crawdad dig his hole,
Honey, baby mine.

5. What you gonna do when the lake runs dry, honey?
What you gonna do when the lake runs dry, babe?
What you gonna do when the lake runs dry?
Sit on the bank and watch the crawdads die,
Honey, baby mine.

6. What you gonna do when the meal gives out, honey?
What you gonna do when the meal gives out, babe?
What you gonna do when the meal gives out?
We'll go visitin' 'round and about,
Honey, baby mine.

7. What you gonna do when the meat's all gone, honey?
What you gonna do when the meat's all gone, babe?
What you gonna do when the meat's all gone?
Sit in the kitchen and gnaw on a bone,
Honey, baby mine.

8. Stuck my hook in a crawdad hole, honey.
Stuck my hook in a crawdad hole, babe.
Stuck my hook in a crawdad hole,
Couldn't get it out to save my soul,
Honey, baby mine.

9. Apple cider, cinnamon beer, honey.
Apple cider, cinnamon beer, babe.
Apple cider, cinnamon beer,
Cold hog's head and possum's ear,
Honey, baby mine.

175

THE FOX

It's not uncommon in folklore to give human characteristics to animals, including the ability to speak. This is a very "cool" fox.

STRUM: Ia

ENGLAND
and
UNITED STATES

Arr. by N. L.

Lively (♩ = 108)

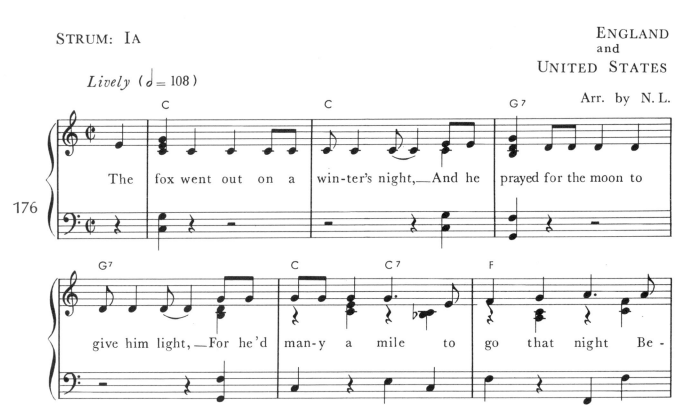

The fox went out on a win-ter's night,—And he prayed for the moon to

give him light,—For he'd man-y a mile to go that night Be-

176

Refrain

fore he'd reach his den, O, Den, O, den, O, be - fore he'd reach his den, —— O, He'd man-y mile to go that night Be - fore he'd reach his den, O.

2. He ran till he came to a farmer's shed
    Where the ducks and the geese were all a bed;
    Said, "A couple of you are gonna be dead
    Before I leave this town O,
    Refrain: Town O, town O,
    Before I leave this town O,
    A couple of you are gonna be dead
    Before I leave this town O."

3. He seized a grey goose by the neck,
    He laid a duck across his back;
    He heeded not their quack, quack, quack,
    And their legs all dangling down O,
    Refrain: Down O, down O,
    Their legs all dangling down O,
    He heeded not their quack, quack, quack,
    And their legs all dangling down O.

4. Then old Mother Slipper Slapper jump'd out of bed,
    And out of the window she cock'd her head,
    Crying "John, John, the grey goose is gone,
    And the fox is over the down O,
    Refrain: Down O, down O,
    The fox is over the down O,
    John, John, the grey goose is gone,
    And the fox is over the down O."

5. Then John ran up to the top of the hill
    Where he blew his horn both loud and shrill;
    And the fox said, "Keep on playin' until
    I get back to my den O,
    Refrain: Den O, den O,
    I get back to my den O,"
    The fox said, "Keep on playin' until
    I get back to my den O."

6. At last he came to his cosy den,
    And there sat his little ones nine or ten;
    And they said, "Dad, you ought to go back again,
    'Cause it sure is a mighty fine town O,
    Refrain: Town O, town O,
    It sure is a mighty fine town O,"
    They said, "Dad, you ought to go back again,
    'Cause it sure is a mighty fine town O."

7. Well, the fox and his wife without any strife
    They cut up the goose without fork or knife,
    They never had such a meal in their life,
    And the little ones chew'd on the bones O,
    Refrain: Bones O, bones O,
    The little ones chew'd on the bones O,
    They never had such a meal in their life,
    And the little ones chew'd on the bones O.

A FROG WENT A COURTIN'

This song dates back to 1580 when "A Most Strange Wedding of the Frog and the Mouse" was licensed at Stationers' Hall in London.

STRUM: IIIA or IA

UNITED STATES

Arr. by N. L.

Moderately (♩ = 74)

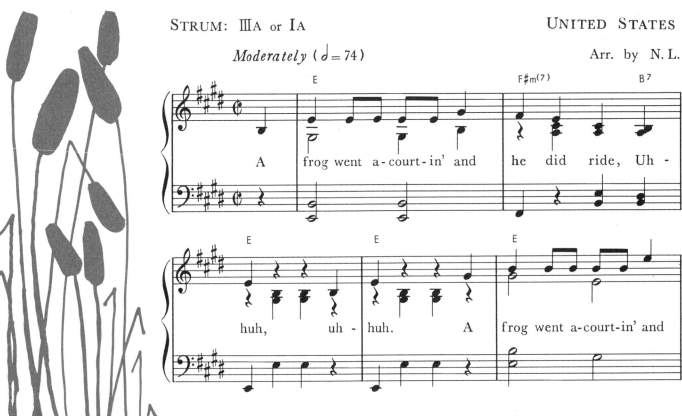

A frog went a-court-in' and he did ride, Uh-huh, uh-huh. A frog went a-court-in' and

he did ride, A sword and pis-tol by his side, Uh-

huh, uh-huh, Uh-huh, uh-huh, uh-huh.

2. He rode up to Miss Mousie's door,
   Uh- huh, uh-huh,
   He rode up to Miss Mousie's door,
   Where he had often been before.
   Uh- huh, uh-huh, uh-huh, uh-huh, uh-huh.

3. "O, Mistress Mouse, are you within?"
   Uh- huh, uh-huh,
   "O, Mistress Mouse, are you within?"
   "I just sat down to weave and spin."
   Uh- huh, uh-huh, uh-huh, uh-huh, uh-huh.

4. He took Miss Mousie on his knee.
   Uh- huh, uh-huh,
   He took Miss Mousie on his knee.
   He said, "Miss Mouse, will you marry me?"
   Uh- huh, uh-huh, uh-huh, uh-huh, uh-huh.

5. "With- out my Uncle Rat's consent,
   Uh- huh, uh-huh,
   "With- out my Uncle Rat's consent,
   I would not marry the President."
   Uh- huh, uh-huh, uh-huh, uh-huh, uh-huh.

6. Uncle Rat laughed till he bust his side,
   Uh- huh, uh-huh,
   Uncle Rat laughed till he bust his side,
   To think that his niece would be a bride.
   Uh- huh, uh-huh, uh-huh, uh-huh, uh-huh.

7. The first guest there was a bumble bee.
   Uh- huh, uh-huh,
   The first guest there was a bumble bee.
   He played the fiddle on his knee.
   Uh- huh, uh-huh, uh-huh, uh-huh, uh-huh.

8. The next guest there was a big grey cat.
   Uh- huh, uh-huh,
   The next guest there was a big grey cat.
   The party didn't last long after that.
   Uh- huh, uh-huh, uh-huh, uh-huh, uh-huh.

9. There's bread and cheese upon the shelf.
   Uh- huh, uh-huh,
   There's bread and cheese upon the shelf.
   So if you're hungry just help yourself.
   Uh- huh, uh-huh, uh-huh, uh-huh, uh-huh.

179

SHOO FLY

The soldiers in the Civil War sang "Shoo fly, don't bother me 'cause I belong to Company G."

180

2. I feel, I feel, I feel like a singing bird. (*twice*)
Refrain

3. I feel, I feel, I feel like a bubbling brook. (*twice*)
Refrain

4. I feel, I feel, I feel like a big sunflow'r. (*twice*)
Refrain

MISTER RABBIT

A little "morality" song.

STRUM: Ia

UNITED STATES

Brightly (♩ = 104)

Arr. by N. L.

Verse

Mis-ter Rab-bit, Mis-ter Rab-bit, your ears' might-y long. "Yes, my Lord, they're put on wrong."

Refrain

Ev-'ry lit-tle soul must shine, —— shine. —— Ev' —— ry lit-tle soul must shine, shine, shine.

182

2. "Mis — ter Rab — bit, Mis — ter Rab — bit, your foot's might — y red.". . . . .
"Yes, my Lord, and I'm al — most dead.". . . . .
Refrain:

3. "Mis — ter Rab — bit, Mis — ter Rab — bit, your coat's might — y grey.". . . . .
"Yes, my Lord, it was made that way.". . . . .
Refrain:

4. "Mis — ter Rab — it, Mis — ter Rab — bit, your tail's might — y white.". . . .
"Yes, my Lord, and I'm gettin' out of sight.". . . . .
Refrain:

THERE
WAS
A
MAN
AND
HE
WAS
MAD

This song is a real delight to young children because of its complete improbability.

UNITED STATES
New Words by W. S.
Arr. by N. L.

STRUM: IVA or IA

Moderately (♩ = 72)

| G | C | G | Em | D7 | G | C | G |

There was a man and he was mad, And he jump'd in-to a pa-per bag.

183

2. The paper bag, it was so thin
That he jumped upon the point of a pin.

3. The point of a pin, it was so sharp
That he jumped upon an Irish harp.

4. The Irish harp, it was so pretty
That he jumped upon a nice little kitty.

5. The nice little kitty began to scratch,
So he jumped into a cabbage patch.

6. The cabbage patch, it was so big
That he jumped upon the back of a pig.

7. The back of the pig began to tickle,
So he jumped upon a big dill pickle.

8. The big dill pickle, it was so sour
That he jumped upon a big sunflower.

9. Along came a bee and stung him on the chin,
And that's the last I've heard of him.

OVER IN THE MEADOW

STRUM: IVA or IA

A counting song.

UNITED STATES
Add. Verses by W. S.
Arr. by N. L.

Moderately (♩ = 92)

O-ver in the mea-dow, in a pond in the sun, Lived an old moth-er frog and her lit-tle frog one.

Pause for counting on fingers

Hop, said the moth-er. I hop, said the one,

Pause for appropriate action

And they hopp'd and were hap-py in their pond in the sun.

184

2. Over in the meadow, in a worn out shoe,
    Lived an old mother cat and her little kittens two. *(count)*
    "Purr," said the mother. "We purr," said the two, *(purr)*
    And they purred and were happy in their worn out shoe.

3. Over in the meadow, in a nest in a tree,
    Lived an old mother bird and her little birdies three. *(count)*
    "Sing," said the mother. "We sing," said the three, *(whistle)*
    And they sang and were happy in their nest in a tree.

4. Over in the meadow, in an old apple core,
    Lived an old mother worm and her little worms four. *(count)*
    "Squirm," said the mother. "We squirm," said the four, *(squirm)*
    And they squirmed and were happy in their old apple core.

5. Over in the meadow, in an old bee hive,
    Lived an old mother bee and her little bees five. *(count)*
    "Buzz," said the mother. "We buzz," said the five, *(buzz)*
    And they buzzed and were happy in their old bee hive.

6. Over in the meadow, in a house made of sticks,
    Lived an old mother dog and her little puppies six. *(count)*
    "Bark," said the mother. "We bark," said the six, *(woof)*
    And they barked and were happy in their house made of sticks.

7. Over in the meadow, in a tree of heaven,
    Lived an old mother owl and her little owls seven. *(count)*
    "Hoot," said the mother. "We hoot," said the seven, *(whoo)*
    And they hooted and were happy in their tree of heaven.

8. Over in the meadow, in an old packing crate,
    Lived an old mother duck and her little ducks eight. *(count)*
    "Quack," said the mother. "We quack," said the eight, *(quack)*
    And they quacked and were happy in their old packing crate.

9. Over in the meadow, in a ball of twine,
    Lived an old mother mouse and her little mousies nine. *(count)*
    "Squeak," said the mother. "We squeak," said the nine, *(eek)*
    And they squeaked and were happy in their ball of twine.

10. Over in the meadow, in a cozy little den,
    Lived an old mother spider and her little spiders ten. *(count)*
    "Spin," said the mother. "We spin," said the ten, *(sewing motion)*
    And they spun and were happy in their cosy little den.

185

SULIRAM

A lullaby has a universal quality in any language. This one says, "Go to sleep, little baby. Now that you're here, I want to keep you with me."

STRUM: IIA

INDONESIA

Arr. by N. L.

Moderately and smoothly (♩=69)

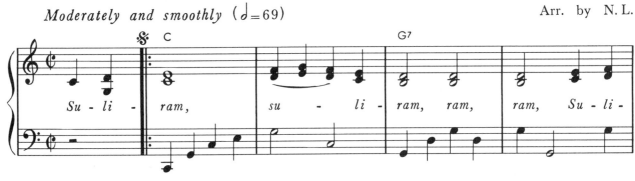

Su - li - ram, su - li - ram, ram, ram, Su - li-

186

ram yang ma - nis, ___ A - du hai in-

dung suh - oor - ang. ___ Bi - dja - kla sa - na di-

187

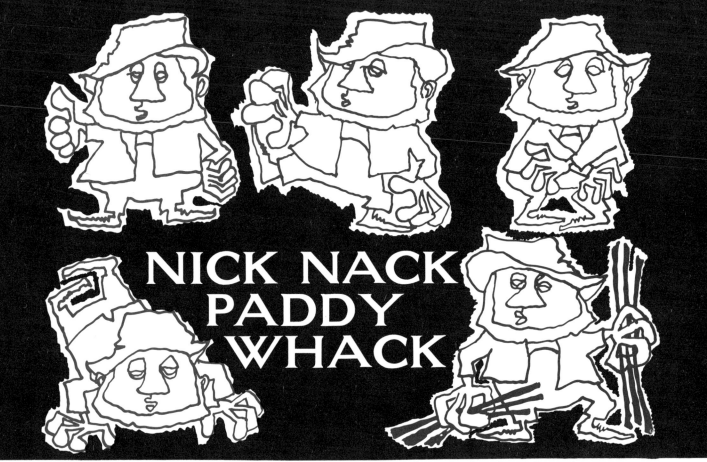

NICK NACK PADDY WHACK

An infectious tune from the North Country of England dating back to the eighteenth century.
It is sung widely throughout Great Britain as well as America.

STRUM: IA

ENGLAND

Arr. by N. L.

188

2. This old man, he did two.
   He did nick nack on his shoe,
   Refrain

3. This old man, he did three.
   He did nick nack on his knee,
   Refrain

4. This old man, he did four.
   He did nick nack on the floor,
   Refrain

5. This old man, he did five.
   Goodness gracious sakes alive!
   Refrain

6. This old man, he did six.
   He did nick nack with some sticks,
   Refrain

WHITE CORAL BELLS

An American version
of a Round which is
English in origin.

UNITED STATES

Moderately slow (♩ = 76)

1 White cor-al bells up-on a slen-der stalk,

2 Li-lies of the val-ley deck my gar-den walk. Oh, don't you wish that

you could hear them ring? That will on-ly hap-pen when the fair-ies sing.

189

CAN YE SEW CUSHIONS

Part lullaby, part "tickling" song, this dates back to the eighteenth century.

STRUM: IIB

SCOTLAND

Arr. by N. L.

Moderately slow (♩=88)

Oh, can ye sew cush-ions And can ye sew sheets, And

can ye_ sing_ ba-lu-loo_ When the bairn greets? And

hie and baw bird-ie, And hie and baw lamb, And

hie and baw bird-ie, My bon-nie wee lamb.

Faster (♩=126) *Refrain*

Hee - o - wee - o, what will I do wi' ye? Black's the life that
I lead wi' ye. Ma - ny o' ye, lit - tle for to gi' ye,
Hee - o - wee - o, what will I do wi' ye?

2. I   biggit* the cradle all on the tree top
And the wind it did blaw, and the cradle did rock.
And   hie and baw birdie, And hie and baw lamb,
And   hie and baw birdie, My bonnie wee lamb.
Refrain

3. Now   hush-a-ba, lammie, and hush-a-ba, dear,
Now   hush-a-ba, lammie, thy minnie† is here.
And   hie and baw birdie, And hie and baw lamb,
And   hie and baw birdie, My bonnie wee lamb.
Refrain

4. The   wild wind is ravin', thy minnie's heart's sair;
The   wild wind is ravin', and you dinna care.
And   hie and baw birdie, And hie and baw lamb,
And   hie and baw birdie, My bonnie wee lamb.
Refrain

5. Sing   ba-la-loo, lammie, sing ba-la-loo, dear,
Does the wee lammie ken that his daddie's no' here?
And   hie and baw birdie, And hie and baw lamb,
And   hie and baw birdie, My bonnie wee lamb.
Refrain

6. Ye're rockin' fu' sweetly upon my warm knee,
But your daddie's a-rockin' upon the salt sea.
And   hie and baw birdie, And hie and baw lamb,
And   hie and baw birdie, My bonnie wee lamb.
Refrain

    * biggit: built
    † minnie: mother

191

STRUM: IX

SWEDEN
Eng. lyrics and
Arr. by N. L.

Freely ($\quad$ = 92)

* Em ___ C ___ Em⁶ ___ Am⁶ ___ Em ___ C ___ D ___ Em

{ Slum-ber time is   draw-ing near,   Night is gath-'ring___ round us. }
{ Stars will all be   bright and clear   When the sand-man has found us. }

Em ___ Em⁷ ___ C ___ Bm ___ Em ___ Em⁷

192

Dream sweet dreams the   long night___ through,   Moth - er   will   be

Am ___ Bm ___ Em ___ Am ___ D ___ Em

near to ___ you.   Go to   sleep, my   dear   one.

* Use E in bass for all guitar chords in first four measures.

SAGAS
ANCIENT AND MODERN

THE MERRY GOLDEN TREE

As in its seventeenth century ancestor "The Golden Vanity," this traditional version ends tragically. While there is a tremendous variation in tune and text in the many versions found all over the English speaking world, one element is always the same— the duplicity of the captain.

STRUM: IX

UNITED STATES

Arr. by N. L.

194

Freely (♩=84)

There was a lit-tle ship, and she sail'd on the sea, And the name of the ship was the Mer-ry Gol-den Tree, And she sail'd on the lone-ly lone-some wa-ter, And she sail'd on the lone-some sea

(♩) ♩ ♩ ♩ ♩ ♩ ♩ ♩

2. There was an — oth — er ship, and she sail'd on the sea,
   And the name of the ship was The Turk — ish Rob — ber — y.
   And she sailed on the lone — ly, etc.

3. There was a lit — tle sail — or boy un — to the Cap — tain said;
   "O, Cap — tain, O, Cap — tain, what will you give to me,
   If I sink her in the lonely," etc.

4. "Two hun — dred gold — en dol — lars I will give un — to thee,
   And my young — est pret — ty daugh — ter for your wed — ded wife to be,
   If you'll sink her in the lonely," etc.

5. O, it's down in — to the waves, and a — way swam he.
   He swam un — til he came to The Turk — ish Rob — ber — y
   Where she sailed in the lonely, etc.

6. Then out of his pock — et an aug — er he drew,
   And he bor'd nine holes for to let the wat — er thru.
   And he sunk her in the lonely, etc.

7. He turned up — on his breast, and back swam he.
   He swam un — til he came to the Mer — ry Gold — en Tree,
   Where she sail'd on the lonely, etc.

8. "O, Cap — tain, O, Cap — tain, won't you take me on board?
   O, Cap — tain, O, Cap — tain, won't you be good as your word,
   For I've sunk her in the lonely," etc.

9. "Oh, I will not take you in," the Cap — tain he re — plied,
   "For you shall ne — ver have my pret — ty daugh — ter for your bride.
   And I'm sail — ing on the lonely," etc.

SIR PATRICK SPENS

STRUM: XIV

SCOTLAND

Vigorously ($\quad = 152$)

Arr. by N. L.

The King sits in Dum- fer -line town, drink-ing the blood-red

196

wine, O; "O,— where will I get a skeel - y skip-per to—

sail this ship of mine, O? O,— where will I get a

skeel - y skip - per to ___ sail this ship of mine, O?"

2. Then up and spake an elder knight, sat at the King's right knee,........................
   "Sir Patrick Spens is the best sailor that ever sailed the sea."....................(repeat)

3. Our king has written a broad letter, and signed it with his hand,...................
   And sent it to Sir Patrick Spens, was a-walking on the sand......................(repeat)

4. "To Noroway, to Noroway, to Noroway o'er the foam;.........................
   The King's daughter of Noroway, 'tis thou must bring her home."..................(repeat)

5. The first word that Sir Patrick read, a loud laugh laughed he.....................
   The next word that Sir Patrick read, a tear did blind his e'e......................(repeat)

6. "O, who is this has done this deed, this ill deed done to me,.....................
   To send us out this time o' year to sail upon the sea?".........................(repeat)

7. They hoisted their sails on a Monenday morn, with all the speed they may,..............
   And they have landed in Noroway upon a Wednesday.........................(repeat)

8. "Make ready, make ready, my merry men a'; our good ship sails in the morn."............
   "O, say not so, my master dear. I fear a deadly storm."........................(repeat)

9. "I saw the new moon late yestere'en, with the old moon in her arm,..................
   And if we go to sea, master, I fear we'll come to harm."........................(repeat)

10. They had not sail'd a league, a league, a league but barely three,...................
    When the light grew dark and the wind grew loud, and gurly grew the sea..........(repeat)

11. The anchors brak, the topmasts snapt, it was such a terrible storm,..................
    And the waves came over the broken ship till a' her sides were torn................(repeat)

12. O, loth, O, loth were our good Scots lords to wet their corkheeled shoon,................
    But long ere a' the play was play'd, they wet their hats aboon.....................(repeat)

13. And many was the feather bed that flutter'd on the foam,........................
    And many was the good lord's son that never more came home....................(repeat)

14. O, long, long may the ladies sit, with their fans into their hand,...................
    Before they see Sir Patrick Spens come sailing to the strand....................(repeat)

15. And long, long may the maidens sit, with their gold combs in their hair,................
    Awaiting for their own dear loves, for them they'll see na mair...................(repeat)

16. Half ower, half ower to Aberdeen, 'tis fifty fathoms deep, O,.....................
    And there lies good Sir Patrick Spens with the Scots lords at his feet, O.............(repeat)

LITTLE BILLEE

Thackeray set these verses to this French tune. A very lighthearted approach to a gruesome situation, thankfully with a happy ending.

STRUM: IX-C

ENGLAND
and
FRANCE

Eng. version by Wm. Makepeace Thackeray

Arr. by N. L.

198

2. (*Solo*) But first with beef and captain's biscuits,
   (*All*) But first with beef and captain's biscuits,
   (*Solo*) And pickled pork they loaded she,
   (*All*) And pickled pork they loaded she.

3. (*Solo*) There was gorging Jack and guzzling Jimmy,
   (*All*) There was gorging Jack and guzzling Jimmy,
   (*Solo*) And the youngest, he was little Billee,
   (*All*) And the youngest, he was little Billee.

4. (*Solo*) Now when they got to the Equator,
   (*All*) Now when they got to the Equator,
   (*Solo*) They'd nothing left but one split pea.
   (*All*) They'd nothing left but one split pea.

5. (*Solo*) Says gorging Jack to guzzling Jimmy,
   (*All*) Says gorging Jack to guzzling Jimmy,
   (*Solo*) "I am extremely hungaree.
   (*All*) I am extremely hungaree."

6. (*Solo*) To gorging Jack says guzzling Jimmy,
   (*All*) To gorging Jack says guzzling Jimmy,
   (*Solo*) "We've nothing left, us must eat we.
   (*All*) We've nothing left, us must eat we."

7. (*Solo*) "There's little Bill, he's young and tender.
   (*All*) There's little Bill, he's young and tender.
   (*Solo*) We're old and tough, so let's eat he.
   (*All*) We're old and tough, so let's eat he."

8. (*Solo*) "Oh! Billy, we're going to kill and eat you.
   (*All*) Oh! Billy, we're going to kill and eat you.
   (*Solo*) Undo the buttons of your chemie.
   (*All*) Undo the buttons of your chemie."

9. (*Solo*) When Bill received this information,
   (*All*) When Bill received this information,
   (*Solo*) He used his pocket handkerchie.
   (*All*) He used his pocket handkerchie.

10. (*Solo*) "First, let me say my catechism,
    (*All*) First, let me say my catechism,
    (*Solo*) Which my poor mammy taught to me,
    (*All*) Which my poor mammy taught to me."

11. (*Solo*) "Make haste, make haste," says guzzling Jimmy,
    (*All*) "Make haste, make haste," says guzzling Jimmy,
    (*Solo*) While Jack pulled out his snickersnee.
    (*All*) While Jack pulled out his snickersnee.

12. (*Solo*) So Billy clambered up the main mast,
    (*All*) So Billy clambered up the main mast,
    (*Solo*) And down he fell on bended knee,
    (*All*) And down he fell on bended knee.

13. (*Solo*) He scarce had come to the twelfth commandment,
    (*All*) He scarce had come to the twelfth commandment,
    (*Solo*) When up he jumps. "There's land I see!"
    (*All*) When up he jumps. "There's land I see!"

14. (*Solo*) "Jerusalem and Madagascar,
    (*All*) Jerusalem and Madagascar,
    (*Solo*) And North and South Amerikee,
    (*All*) And North and South Amerikee."

15. (*Solo*) "A British flag is riding at anchor,
    (*All*) A British flag is riding at anchor,
    (*Solo*) With Adm'ral Napier, K.C.B.,
    (*All*) With Adm'ral Napier, K.C.B."

16. (*Solo*) So when they got aboard the Adm'ral's,
    (*All*) So When they got aboard the Adm'ral's,
    (*Solo*) He hang'd fat Jack and flogged Jimmee.
    (*All*) He hang'd fat Jack and flogged Jimmee.

17. (*Solo*) But as for little Bill, he made him
    (*All*) But as for little Bill, he made him
    (*Solo*) The captain of a seventy three,
    (*All*) The captain of a seventy three.

THE TITANIC

An incongruously spirited tune for the telling of this maritime tragedy. Since the sinking in 1912, it's been the subject of innumerable folk tales and ballads.

STRUM: VA or IA

UNITED STATES

Oh, they built the ship Ti - tan - ic to sail the o - cean
blue, And they thought they had a ship that the
wa - ter would ne - ver go thru, But the Lord's al - might - y
hand knew that ship would ne - ver land; It was
sad___ when that great___ ship went down._____

Refrain

It was sad,_____ it was sad,_____
___ It was sad when that great___ ship went

(to the bot-tom of the sea)

down. _____ Hus-bands and

wives, lit-tle child-ren lost their lives. It was

sad___ when that great___ ship went down. _____

2. Oh, they sailed from Eng—land and were al — most to the shore, ...
   When the rich re — fused to as — so-ci-ate with the pore. .....
   So they put them down be — low, where they were the first to go. ....
   It was sad when that great ship went down. ....
   Refrain:

3. The boat was full of sin, and the sides a — bout to burst, ...
   When the cap — tain shout — ed, "A — wo-men and chil—dren first!" ....
   Oh, the cap—tain tried to wire, but the lines were all on fire. ......
   It was sad, *etc.*
   Refrain:

4. Oh, they swung the life — boats out o'er the deep and rag — ing sea, ...
   When the band struck up with "A — Nearer My God To Thee." ....
   Lit — tle chil—dren wept and cried as the waves swept o'er the side. .....
   It was sad, *etc.*
   Refrain:

EDWARD

The theme of fratricide, as it occurs in the next two songs, permeates almost every culture in the world. As ancient as the story of Abel and Cain, or Joseph and his brothers, the feelings these songs arouse are still recognizable to contemporary audiences.

STRUM: IX

UNITED STATES

Arr. by N. L.

"How — came this blood — on your shirt sleeve? O, dear son, tell

me." "It is the blood of my old — grey - hound that —

traced the fox for — me, for me, that — traced the fox for me."

202

2. "It   is too pale for your grey hound
           Oh, dear son, tell me."
"It   is the blood of my old grey horse
That plowed the field for me, for me,
That plowed the field for me."

3. "It   is too pale for your grey horse.
           Oh, dear son, tell me."
"It   is the blood of my youngest brother
Who walked the road with me, with me,
Who walked the road with me.

4. "And it's what did you fall out about?
           Oh, dear son, tell me."
"We fell out about a holly bush
That might have made a tree, a tree,
That might have made a tree."

5. "And it's what will you do now, my son?
           Oh, dear son, tell me."
"I'll set my foot in yonder ship
And I'll sail over the sea, the sea,
And I'll sail over the sea."

6. "And when will you return, my son?
           Oh, dear son, tell me."
"When moon and sun set in yonder hill,
And that will never be, be, be,
And that will never be."

THE MURDERED BROTHER

This may well pre-date the "Edward" version. Many scholarly studies have been
made which bear out this contention.

STRUM: IVc or IIc

DENMARK

Eng. version by W.S.
Arr. by N.L.

Slowly (♩.= 52)

"Where have you been such a long time? Son, oh now tell me." ___ "Oh
Hvor har du vae-ret saa laen-ge? Svend i Ro-sens-gaard! ___ Og

I've been down in the mead-ow, gen-tle moth-er mine. ___ I
jeg har vae-ret i en ___ ge, kae-re mo-der vor. ___ I

won-der shall I ev-er come home a-gain?"
ven-te mig sent ell-er al-drig.

204

2. "Why runs your sword so bloody?
     Son, oh, now tell me."
   "Oh, I have murder'd my brother,
     Gentle mother mine.
     I wonder shall I ever come home again."

3. "Is there a place you can hide in?
     Son, oh, now tell me."
   "I'll sail far over the waters,
     Gentle mother", *etc.*

4. "And when again shall I see you?
     Son, oh, now tell me."
   "When ev'ry woman's a widow,
     Gentle mother", *etc.*

5. "When will all women be widows?
     Son, oh, now tell me."
   "When ev'ry man has been murdered,
     Gentle mother", *etc.*

6. "When will all men be murdered?
     Son, oh, now tell me."
   "When stones shall float in the water,
     Gentle mother", *etc.*

7. "And when will stones be floating?
     Son, oh, now tell me."
   "When feathers sink to the bottom,
     Gentle mother", *etc.*

8. "And when will feathers be sinking?
     Son, oh, now tell me."
   "When mountains all are burning,
     Gentle mother", *etc.*

9. "And when will mountains be burning?
     Son, oh, now tell me."
   "When stars in heaven are dancing,
     Gentle mother", *etc.*

10. "And when will stars be dancing?
      Son, oh, now tell me."
    "When earth has seen the last judgment,
      Gentle mother", *etc.*

2. Hvorfor er dit sværd saa blodigt?
   Svend i Rosensgaard!
   For jeg har dræbt min broder.
   Kære moder, *etc.*

3. Hvor vil du dig hen vende?
   Svend i Rosensgaard!
   Jeg vil af landet rende.
   Kære moder, *etc.*

4. Naar vil du dig hjem vende?
   Svend i Rosensgaard!
   Naar alle kvinder bliver enke.
   Kære moder, *etc.*

5. Naar bliver alle kvinder enke?
   Svend i Rosensgaard!
   Naar alle mænd bliver døde.
   Kære moder, *etc.*

6. Naar bliver alle mænd døde?
   Svend i Rosensgaard!
   Naar huse og gaarde bliver øde.
   Kære moder, *etc.*

7. Naar bliver huse og gaarde øde?
   Svend i Rosensgaard!
   Naar vi ser fjedren synke.
   Kære moder, *etc.*

8. Naar ser vi fjedren synke?
   Svend i Rosensgaard!
   Naar vi ser stenen flyde.
   Kære moder, *etc.*

9. Naar ser vi stenen flyde?
   Svend i Rosensgaard!
   Naar vi ser havet brænde.
   Kære moder, *etc.*

10. Naar ser vi havet brænde?
    Svend i Rosensgaard!
    Naar vi ser verdens ende.
    Kære moder, *etc.*

205

ROBIN HOOD AND THE TANNER

There are a dozen versions of this theme in ballads about Robin Hood: meeting a stranger, fighting, losing, and inviting him to join the "Merry Men." Obviously Robin's a good loser.

STRUM: IB

ENGLAND

Arr. by N. L.

Lively - With spirit ($\dot{\ } = 60$)

206

Bold Ar - der went forth one sum - mer morn - ing, To view___ the mer - ry green wood; For to hunt for the deer___ that run here and there, And

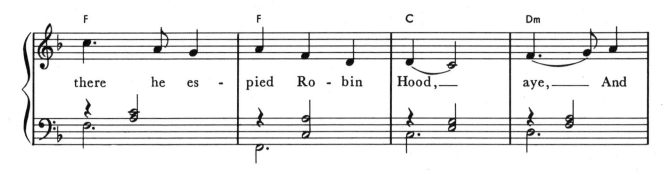

there he es - pied Ro - bin Hood, __ aye, __ And

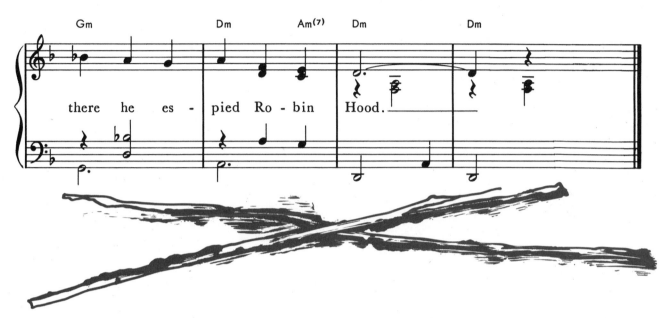

there he es - pied Ro - bin Hood. __

2. "What fellow art thou?" Quoth bold Robin Hood,
   "And what is thy business here?
     For now, to be brief, thou dost look like a thief,
     And come for to steal the king's deer. Aye!
     And come for to steal the king's deer."

3. "No, I am the keeper of this parish,
     The king, he hath put me in trust;
     And therefore I pray thee to get on thy way,
     Or else to upstand thee I must. Aye!
     Or else to upstand thee I must."

4. "Tis thou must have more partakers in store
     Before thou upstand me in deed;
     For I have a staff, he is made of ground graffe,
     And I warrant he'll do my deed. Aye!
     And I warrant he'll do my deed."

5. "And I have another," quoth bold Robin Hood,
   "It's made of an oaken tree;
     He's eight foot and a half and would knock down a calf,
     And why shouldn't it knock down thee. Aye!
     And why shouldn't it knock down thee?"

6. "Let us measure our staves," says bold Robin Hood,
   "Before we begin and away;
     If by half a foot mine should be longer than thine,
     Then that should be counted foul play. Aye!
     Then that should be counted foul play."

7. Then at it they went, for bang, for bang,
     The space of two hours or more;
     Ev'ry blow they did swing made the grove to ring,
     And they played their game so sure. Aye!
     They played their game so sure.

8. Then bold Robin Hood drew forth bugle horn,
     And he blew it both loud and shrill;
     And direct there upon he espied Little John
     Come running a-down the hill. Aye!
     Come running a-down the hill.

9. "O, what is the matter." then said Little John,
   "You are not doing well," he cried;
   "O," says bold Robin Hood, "Here's a tanner so good,
     And I warrant he's tann'd my hide. Aye!
     I warrant he's tann'd my hide."

10. "If he's such a tanner," then says Little John,
    "A tanner that tans so true,
     O, we'll make no doubt but we'll have a fresh bout,
     And I warrant he'll tan my hide too. Aye!
     I warrant he'll tan my hide too."

11. "That thing shall not be," says bold Robin Hood,
    "For he is a hero so bold;
     For he has best play'd; he's master of his trade,
     And by no man shall he be controll'd. Aye!
     By no man shall he be controll'd."

JOHN HENRY

Probably the best-known of American ballads, "John Henry" is a legend which typifies the struggle of man against the machine. It's a ballad of great dignity and strength.

STRUM: Ia

UNITED STATES

Lively (♩ = 120)

Arr. by N. L.

When John Hen-ry was a lit-tle ba-by,

Sit-tin' on his dad-dy's knee, Said "The

Big Bend Tun-nel on the C and O Road And the

ham-mer's gon-na be the death of me, Lord, Lord, And the

ham-mer's gon-na be the death of me."

2. Now the captain said to John Henry,
"Gonna bring me a steam drill 'round.
Gonna take that steam drill out on the job,
Gonna whop that steel on down,
Lord, Lord,
Gonna whop that steel on down."

3. John Henry swung that hammer
An' brought the hammer down.
A man in Chattanooga, miles away,
Said, "Listen to that rumblin' sound,
Lord, Lord,
Just listen to that rumblin' sound."

4. The man who invented the steam drill
Thought he was mighty fine.
John Henry drove about fifteen feet,
And the steam drill only made nine,
Lord, Lord,
And the steam drill only made nine.

5. John Henry was hammerin' on the mountain,
An' his hammer was strikin' fire,
He drove so hard till he broke his pore heart
An' he laid down his hammer an' he died, Lord, Lo
He laid down his hammer an' he died.

6. Oh, they took John Henry to the graveyard,
And buried him in the sand,
And ev'ry locomotive come roarin' by,
Sayin' "There lies a steel drivin' man,
Lord, Lord."
Sayin' "There lies a steel drivin' man."

208

FRAILTIES AND FOIBLES

OLD GRUMBLE

A never-to-be-decided question: who works hardest, he or she? This song dates back to 1825.

STRUM: IVA or IA   UNITED STATES

Moderately fast (♩=90)   Arr. by N. L.

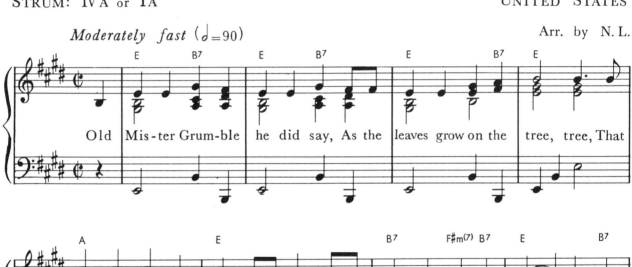

Old Mis-ter Grum-ble he did say, As the leaves grow on the tree, tree, That

he could do more work in a day Than his wife could do in three,— three. That

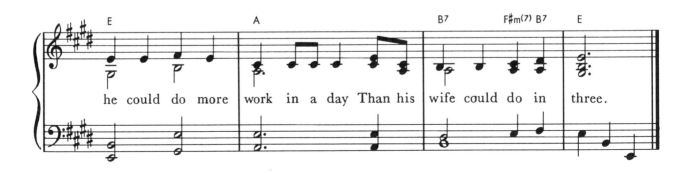

he could do more work in a day Than his wife could do in three.

2. Old   Mistress Grumble she did say,
               "You may do it now, now.
               You may do the work of the house
   And   I'll go follow the plow, plow,
   And   you may do the work of the house
   And   I'll go follow the plow."

3. "For   you must milk the brindle cow
   For   fear that she'll go dry, dry,
   And   you must feed the little pig
   That   stands within the sty, sty.
   And   you must feed the little pig
   That   stands within the sty."

4. "And   you must churn the crock of cream
   That   stands within the frame, frame,
   And   you must watch the fat in the pot
   Or   it'll go up in flame, flame.
   And   you must watch the fat in the pot
   Or   it'll go up in flame."

5. "And   you must reel the skein of yarn
   That   I spun yesterday, day,
   And   you must watch the speckled hen
   Or   she will run away, way.
   And   you must watch the speckled hen
   Or   she will run away."

6. Old   Mistress Grumble took the whip
   And   went to follow the plow, plow.
               Mister Grumble took the pail
   And   went to milk the cow, cow.
   And   Mister Grumble took the pail
   And   went to milk the cow.

7. The   cow she kicked, the cow she jumped,
   The   cow curled up her nose, nose.
   She   hit old Grumble a lick on the chin
   And the blood run down to his toes, toes.
   She   hit old Grumble a lick on the chin
   And the blood run down to his toes.

8. He   went to feed the little pig
   That   stood within the sty, sty.
   He   hit his head against the beam
   And his brains began to fly, fly.
   He   hit his head against the beam
   And his brains began to fly.

9. He   went to churn the crock of cream
   That   stood within the frame, frame,
   But   he forgot the fat in the pot
   And it   all went up in flame, flame.
   And   he forgot the fat in the pot
   And it   all went up in flame.

10. He   went to reel the skein of yarn
   That his wife spun yesterday, day,
   But   he forgot the speckled hen
   And   she did run away, way.
   And   he forgot the speckled hen
   And   she did run away.

11. He   looked to the east, he looked to the west,
   He   looked up to the sun, sun.
   He   swore it was a very long day
   And his wife would never come home, home.
   And he swore it was a very long day
   And his wife would never come home.

12. Old   Mistress Grumble she came home
   And   found him looking sad, sad.
   She   stamped her feet and clapped her hands
   And   said that she was glad, glad.
   She   stamped her feet and clapped her hands
   And   said that she was glad.

13. Old   Mister Grumble he could see
   As the   leaves grew on the tree, tree,
   His   wife could do more work in a day
   Than   he could do in three, three.
   His   wife could do more work in a day
   Than   he could do in three.

211

LA FIROLERA

Very few "about to be" widows
are as outspoken as this one.

STRUM: IB

MEXICO
Eng. version by W. S.
Arr. by N. L.

Brightly (♩ = 192)

Verse

My hus-band, who's dy-ing, still lin-gers,____
Mi ma - rid - o es - ta en la ca - ma,____

And I'm on my knees by his bed.____
Y yo en la ca - be - ce - ra.____

212

____ With my ro - sa - ry here in my fin - gers,____
____ Con el ro - sa - rio en ____ la ma - no,____

____ And I pray that he soon may be dead.____
____ Pi - dien - do le a Di - os que se mue - ra____

2. His heart now no longer is beating,
   His eyes now no longer can see;
   And I hope that the devil is treating
   My old man like he used to treat me.
   Refrain

2. Ya mi marido se murio,
   Y el diablo se lo llevó,
   Ahora se estara pagando
   Las patadas que me dió.

213

THE MILLER'S WILL

Virtue must evidently be its own reward.

STRUM: I-A   UNITED STATES

Lively (♩ = 100)   Arr. by N. L.

Verse

There was an old mil-ler and he lived all a-lone; He had three sons all ful-ly grown,— And when he came to make his will, All he had left was a lit-tle grist mill.

Refrain

Sing fol ding-a dye do, fol ding-a day.

214

(♩)   ♩   ♩   ♩   ♩   ♩   ♩   ♩   (♩)

2. He		call'd	to	him		his	eld —	est	son, ...
Says:		"Son, oh,		son	my	race		is	run; ....
		If	I a	mil — ler		of		you	make, ...
		Pray,	tell	me		what	toll	you'd	take?" ....
Refrain:									
3.		"Fath-er,	oh,	Fath-er,	my	name		is	Bill, ...
And		from	each	bush-el	I'd	take		a	gill; ....
For		here	I	would	my	for —		tune	make, ...
And		that	is the	toll	I	in —	tend	to	take." ...
Refrain:									
4.		"Son, oh,		son,	you	are		a	fool. ....
You		nev — er	have	learn'd	to	fol —	low	my	rule; ....
This		mill	to	you	I	nev —	er	will	give, ...
For		on	such a	toll	you	nev —	er	could	live." ....
Refrain:									
5. He		call'd	to	him		his	sec —	ond	son, ...
Says:		"Son, oh,		son,	my	race		is	run; ....
		If	I a	mil — ler		of		you	make, ...
		Pray,	tell	me		what	toll	you'd	take?" ...
Refrain:									
6.		"Fath-er,	oh,	Fath-er,	my	name		is	Mort, ...
And		from	each	bush-el	I'd	take		a	quart; ......
For		here	I	would	my	for —		tune	make, ...
And		that	is the	toll	I	in —	tend	to	take." ...
7.		"Son, oh,		son,	you	are		a	fool. ....
You		nev — er	have	learn'd	to	fol —	low	my	rule; ....
This		mill	to	you	I	nev —	er	will	give, ...
For		on	such a	toll	you		nev —	er could	live." ....
Refrain:									
8. He		call'd	to	him		his	young —	est	son, ...
Says:		"Son, oh,		son,	my	race		is	run; ....
		If	I a	mil — ler		of		you	make, ...
		Pray,	tell	me		what	toll	you'd	take?" ...
Refrain:									
9.		"Fath-er,	oh,	fath-er,	my	name		is	Paul, ...
And		from	each	bush-el	I'd	take		it	all; ....
I'd		steal	all the	corn	and	swear		to the	sack, ...
And		beat the	old	farm — er	if he	ev —	er	comes	back." ...
Refrain:									
10.		"Glor — y	be to	God,"	the	old		man	says. ....
"There's		one of	my	sons	learn'd to	fol —	low	my	ways!" ....
		"Hal	— le — lu — yah",	his	old		wom —	an	cries, ...
And the		old	man	turns	up his	toes		and	dies. ....
Refrain:									

215

THE TWO SISTERS

Another lively tune with a gruesome text.

STRUM: IIIB or IIB

UNITED STATES

Moderately (♩ = 112)

Arr. by N. L.

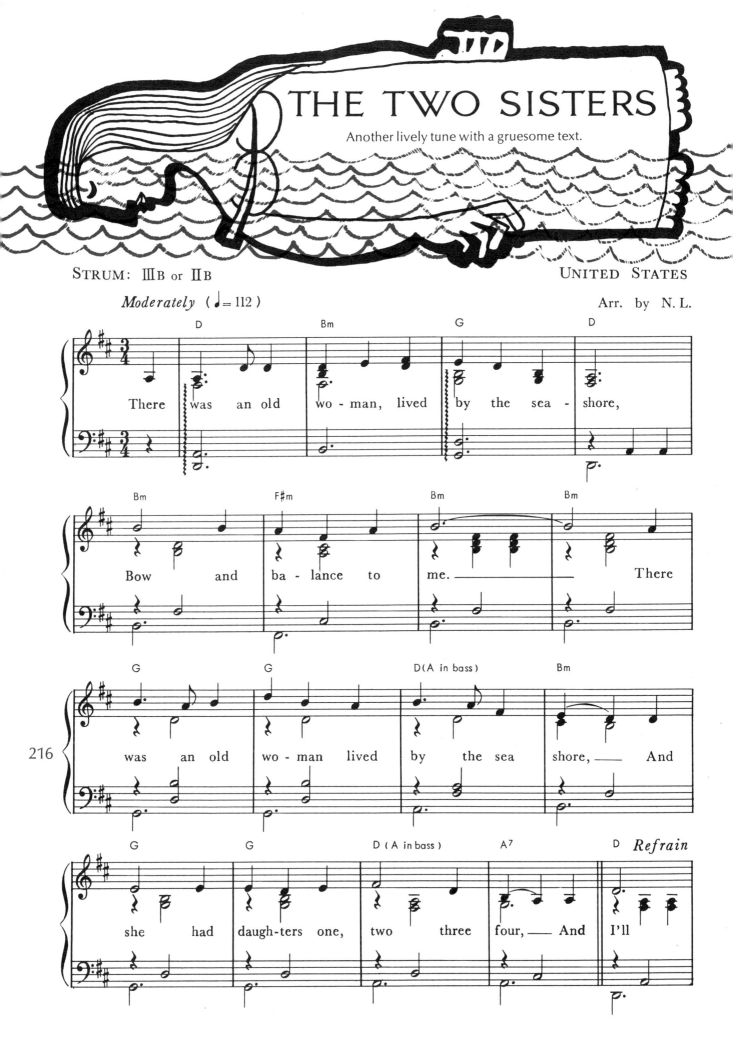

There was an old wo-man, lived by the sea-shore,

Bow and ba-lance to me. _____ There

216 was an old wo-man lived by the sea shore, _____ And

she had daugh-ters one, two three four, _____ And I'll

Refrain

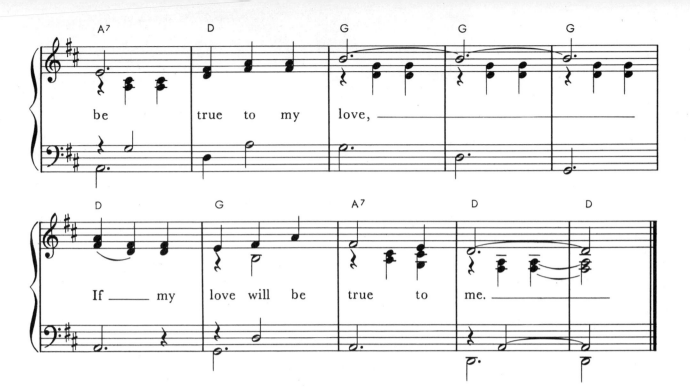

be true to my love, _____ If _____ my love will be true to me. _____

2. A young man he came a-courtin' there then,
   Bow and balance to me.
   A young man he came a-courtin' there then,
   The oldest daughter got stuck on him.
   Refrain

3. He gave the youngest a beaver hat,
   Bow and balance to me.
   He gave the youngest a beaver hat,
   The oldest sister thought hard on that.
   Refrain

4. He gave his love a gay gold ring,
   Bow and balance to me.
   He gave his love a gay gold ring,
   The fam'ly thought it a sinful thing.
   Refrain

5. "O, sister dear, let's we walk out."
   Bow and balance to me.
   "O, sister dear, let's we walk out,
   And see the ships go sailing about."
   Refrain

6. And as they passed the salty brim,
   Bow and balance to me.
   And as they passed the salty brim,
   The ugly one pushed the fair one in.
   Refrain

7. "O, sister dear, pray lend me your hand."
   Bow and balance to me.
   "O, sister dear, pray lend me your hand,
   And you may have Willie and all his land."
   Refrain

8. "I'll neither lend thee hand nor glove."
   Bow and balance to me.
   "I'll neither lend thee hand nor glove,
   But I will have your own true love."
   Refrain

9. Sometimes she sank and sometimes she swam,
   Bow and balance to me.
   Sometimes she sank and sometimes she swam,
   Until she came to the old mill dam.
   Refrain

10. The miller got out his fishing hook,
    Bow and balance to me.
    The miller got out his fishing hook,
    And fished the maiden right out of the brook.
    Refrain

11. He robb'd her of her gay gold ring,
    Bow and balance to me.
    He robb'd her of her gay gold ring,
    And then he pushed her in again.
    Refrain

12. The miller was hung for what he did take,
    Bow and balance to me.
    The miller was hung for what he did take,
    And the oldest sister was burn'd at the stake.
    Refrain

217

THE VICAR OF BRAY

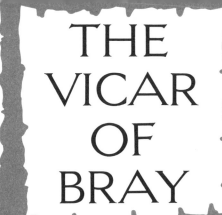

A song which punctures the balloon of pompous opportunism – in this case, wearing the garb of the clergy.

STRUM: IA

ENGLAND

Arr. by N. L.

Moderately fast and jauntily (♩ =160)

In good King_ Charles -'s gold - en days, when loy - al - ty no harm meant, A zeal - ous_ high church - man I was, and so I gain'd pre - fer - ment. To teach my flock I nev - er miss'd: Kings are by_ God ap - poin - ted, And

218

damned are—those who dare re-sist, or touch the Lord's a-noint-ed.

Refrain

And this is law, I will main-tain, un-til my—dy-ing—day, Sir, That what-so-ev-er king shall reign, I'll still be the Vi-car of Bray, Sir!

2. When royal James obtain'd the crown and popery came in fashion,
   The penal laws I hooted down and read the declaration.
   The Church of Rome I found would fit full well my constitution,
   And I had been a Jesuit but for the revolution.
Refrain:

3. When William was our king declar'd to heal the nation's grievance,
   With this new wind about I steer'd and swore to him allegiance.
   Old principles I did revoke, set conscience at a distance,
   Passive resistance was a joke, a jest was nonresistance.
Refrain:

4. When George in pudding time came o'er, and moderate men look'd big, Sir,
   I turn'd the "cat in pan" once more, and so became a Whig, Sir.
   And this preferment I procured from our new faith's defender,
   And almost ev'ry day abjured the Pope and the Pretender.
Refrain:

5. The illustrious House of Hanover and Protestant succession,
   To these I lustily will swear while they can keep possession.
   For in my faith and loyalty I never once will falter,
   And George my lawful king shall be, except the times should alter.
Refrain:

"Spinn, Spinn," is an early nineteenth century version of the same story as
"Whistle, Daughter, Whistle."

GERMANY

Eng. Version by W. S.
Arr. by N. L.

STRUM: IB

Moderately fast (♩ = 138)

"Spin, spin, my be - lov - ed daugh - ter, and you'll get new
„Spinn, spinn, mei - ne lie - be Toch - ter, Ich kauf dir'n Paar

shoes," "Oh, good, my be - lov - ed moth - er, what won - der - ful
Schuh." Ach ja, mei - ne lie - be Mu - tter, auch Schnallen da -

news. But how can I spin when my fing - er is
zu. Ich kann ja nicht spinn - en es schmerzt mich mein

sore? It hurts, it hurts, I can spin no more."
Finger Und thut, it und thut, I und thut mir so weh".

220

2. Spin, spin, my beloved daughter, and you'll get new hose.
   "Oh, good, my beloved mother, I need them, God knows.
   But how," *etc.*

3. Spin, spin, my beloved daughter, and you'll get a hat.
   "Oh, good, my beloved mother, I'd surely like that.
   But how," *etc.*

4. Spin, spin, my beloved daughter, and you'll catch a man.
   "Oh, good, my beloved mother, I hope that I can.
   It's strange, but my finger that just was so sore,
   It hurts, it hurts, it hurts me no more."

Spinn, spinn, meine liebe Tochter; Ich kauf' dir'n Paar Schuh.
„Ach ja, meine liebe Mutter, auch Schnallen dazu!
Ich kann ja nicht spinnen, es schmerzt mir mein Finger,
Und thut, und thut, und thut mir so weh."

221

Spinn, spinn, meine liebe Tochter; Ich kauf' dir'n Paar Strümpf'.
„Ach ja, meine liebe Mutter, schöne Zwicklein darin!
Ich kann ja nicht spinnen," *u. s. w.*

Spinn, spinn, meine liebe Tochter; Ich kauf' dir ein Kleid.
„Ach ja, meine liebe Mutter, nicht zu eng und nicht zu weit!
Ich kann ja nicht spinnen," *u. s. w.*

Spinn, spinn, meine liebe Tochter; Ich kauf' dir ein'n Mann.
„Ach ja, meine liebe Mutter, der steht mir wohl an!
Nun kann ich schon spinnen, es schmerzt mir kein Finger,
Und thut, und thut, und thut mir nicht weh!"

OH DEAR MAMA,
I'M FEELING SO BADLY

This girl is a bit testy until her mother comes up with the right offer.

STRUM: IVc

ITALY

Eng. version by W. S.
Arr. by N. L.

Moderately fast (♩.= 92)

"Oh, dear Ma - ma, I'm feel - ing so bad - ly. Go to the
Ca - ra mam - ma, io so - no ma - la - ta. Ma un - a

gar - den and find me a cure." "Yes, my daugh - ter, I'll pick you some
co - sa nell-'or - to ci sta. "E nell- 'or - to ci sta-l'in - sa-

let - tuce, And it will make you feel bet - ter, I'm sure." "Oh, Ma - ma,
la - ta, Se tu la vuo - i io te la do". O, mam-ma,

No! No! No! That would be bad for me, Ma - ma, I
no, no, no. Quest - o fa ma - le, pel ma - le che

know. Why can't you stop be-ing stu-pid and get me Some-thing that's
ho. O quant' e stu-pi-da la mam-ma mi - a, Che non con -

good for me and won't up - set me? Oh, Ma-ma, No! No!
os - ce la ma-lat ti - a, O, mam-ma, no, no,

No! That would be bad for me, Ma-ma, I know."
no. Quest-o fa ma-le pel ma-le che ho.

*Verses 2 and 3: parsley, garlic, peppers, apples, etc.

4. "O, dear Mama, I'm feeling so badly. Go to the garden and find me a cure."
"Yes, my daughter, I'll bring you the gard'ner, And he will make you feel better, I'm sure".
"O, Mama, yes! Yes! Yes! That is exactly the thing that I need.
Where in the world is there such a fine mother, Search as I might I could ne'er find another.
O, Mama, Yes! Yes! Yes! Go find the gard'ner and bring him with speed."

*Verses 2 and 3: la papapa (potatoes), il pomidoro (tomatoes)

4. Cara mamma, io sono malata.　　　　Questo va bene per farmi guari!
   Ma una cosa nell'orto ci sta!　　　　O quant'e cara la mamma mia,
   E nell'orto ci sta l'ortolano,　　　　Che conosciuto la malattia!
   Se tu lo vuoi, io te lo do!　　　　　O mamma, si! Si! Si!
   O mamma, si! Si! Si!　　　　　　　Questo va bene per farmi guari!

WHISTLE, DAUGHTER, WHISTLE

This Southern mountain song as well as "Spin, Spin" and "O, Dear Mama," indicate that, when it comes to getting a man, nothing is impossible.

STRUM: IIA

UNITED STATES

Arr. by N. L.

Mother, I would marry. Yes, I would be a bride; And
I would have a young man for-ev-er at my side;—— For
if I had a young man, oh, how hap-py I would be,—— For
I am tired and wea-ry of my sing-u-la-ri-ty.

224

2. "Whis — tle, daugh — ter, whis — tle, and you shall have a cow.".......
   I can — not whis — tle, Moth — er. I guess I don't know how,.......
   But if I had a young man, *etc.*

3. "Whis — tle, daugh — ter, whis — tle, and you shall have a sheep.".....
   I can — not whis — tle, Moth — er, for I can on — ly weep,......
   But if I had a young man, *etc.*

4. "Whis — tle, daugh — ter, whis — tle, and you shall have a man.".....
   I can — not whis — tle, Moth — er. (whistle rest of line.........
   "You stub — born lit — tle daugh—ter, what makes you whis — tle now?".....
   I'd ra — ther whis — tle for a man than for a sheep or cow.........

THE SHEER JOY OF SINGING

LINCOLNSHIRE POACHER

Poaching has always been a way of life as well as a means of getting food. This is a bright, lusty ballad.

STRUM: VIC or IC

ENGLAND

Arr. by N. L.

Sprightly (♩.=108)

When I was bound apprentice in famous Lincolnshire, Full

well I served my master for more than seven year, Till

I took up to poaching, as you shall quickly hear.

Refrain

Oh, 'tis my delight on a shining night in the season of the year.

226

2. As me and my companions were setting of a snare,
   'Twas then we spied the gamekeeper; for him we did not care,
   For we can wrestle and fight, my boys, and jump out anywhere.
   Oh, 'tis my delight, *etc.*

3. As me and my companions were setting four or five,
   And taking 'em on up again, we caught a hare alive.
   We took a hare alive, my boys, and through the woods did steer.
   Oh, 'tis my delight, *etc.*

4. I threw him on my shoulder, and then we trudged home;
   We took him to a neighbor's house and sold him for a crown.
   We sold him for a crown, my boys, but I did not tell you where.
   Oh, 'tis my delight, *etc.*

5. Success to ev'ry gentleman that lives in Lincolnshire.
   Success to ev'ry poacher that wants to sell a hare.
   Bad luck to ev'ry gamekeeper that will not sell his deer.
   Oh, 'tis my delight, *etc.*

GOOBER PEAS

What better way to get rid of complaints than to sing about them. The "Goober Peas"
in this Confederate Army song are really peanuts.

STRUM: IXA or IA

UNITED STATES

Moderately (♩ = 108)

Arr. by N. L.

228

Sit - ting by the road - side on a sum - mer day, Chat - ting with my mess - mates,

pass - ing time a - way, Ly - ing in the shad - ow un - der - neath the trees,

Refrain

Good-ness, how de-li-cious, eat-ing goo-ber peas.

Peas, peas, peas, peas!

Eat-ing goo-ber peas.

Good-ness, how de-li-cious, eat-ing goo-ber peas!

2. When a horseman passes, the soldiers have a rule
   To cry out at their loudest, "Mister, here's your mule";
   But another pleasure enchantinger than these
   Is wearing out your grinders, eating goober peas!
   Refrain

3. Just before the battle the Gen'ral hears a row.
   He says, "The Yanks are coming, I hear their rifles now."
   He turns around in wonder, and what d'you think he sees?
   The Georgia Militia, eating goober peas!
   Refrain

4. I think my song has lasted almost long enough.
   The subject's interesting, but rhymes are mighty rough.
   I wish this war was over, when, free from rags and fleas,
   We'd kiss our wives and sweethearts, and gobble goober peas!
   Refrain

229

THAT'S A LIE

Known also as the "Derby Ram," this is supposed to have been a favorite of George Washington. This particular version is a forecastle shanty.

STRUM: IVc or Ic

BRITISH ISLES
and
NORTH AMERICA

Arr. by N. L.

Lively (♩.=112)

Verse

As I went down to Der-by, 'twas on a mar-ket day, I

met the fin-est ram, sir, that ev-er was fed up-on hay.

Refrain

That's a lie, that's a lie, that's a lie, a lie, a lie.

230

(♪) 𝅘𝅥𝅮.   𝅘𝅥𝅮.   𝅘𝅥𝅮.   𝅘𝅥𝅮.   𝅘𝅥𝅮.   𝅘𝅥𝅮.   𝅘𝅥𝅮. 𝅘𝅥𝅮

2. This ram   and I   got drunk, Sir, as drunk   as   we   could be, ...
    And when   we so — ber'd up, Sir, we were far   a — way   out   on   the   sea.
Refrain:

3. This won — der — ful   old ram, Sir, was play — ful   as   a   kid; . . . . . .
    He swal — low'd the   Cap — tain's spy — glass, a — long with the   bo — sun's lid.
Refrain:

4. One morn — ing   on   the poop — deck, be — fore   eight bells   was   rung, ...
    He grabb'd the   Cap — tain's sex — tant   and took   a   shot at the   sun.
Refrain:

5. The night   was wet   and rough, Sir. The wind   was   sharp as   steel. . . . . .
    He bor — row'd my   suit   of   oil — skins, and took   my   trick at the   wheel.
Refrain:

6. The crew   a — board this ship, Sir, are hand — some, strong   and   brave; . . . .
    The fin — est   lot   of   sail — ors   that ev — er   sail'd o — ver the   wave.
Refrain:

Alternate last verse for landlubbers:

7. The peo — ple   in   this room, Sir, are hand — some, brave   and   strong, . . .
    The fin — est group of   sing — ers   ev — er   to   sing   a   song.
Refrain:

231

CAPTAIN JINKS

First known here in 1869, this song has no relationship with any particular period. It's just a parody on Army life generally.

STRUM: IVC or IC

UNITED STATES

Moderately (♩.= 92)

Verse

Arr. by N.L.

I'm Cap-tain Jinks of the Horse Ma-rines, I feed my horse on corn and beans, And

sport young la-dies in their 'teens, Tho' a Cap-tain in the Ar-my I

teach the la-dies how to dance, How to dance, how to dance, I

C | **C G** | **A7** | **D7**

teach the la - dies how to dance, For I'm the pet of the Ar - my.

Refrain

G | **G** | **D7** | **G D7 G**

I'm Cap-tain Jinks of the Horse Ma-rines, I feed my horse on corn and beans, And

G | **G** | **D7** | **G**

of - ten live be - yond my means, Tho' a Cap-tain in the Ar - my.

2. I joined my corps when twenty-one;
   Of course, I thought it capital fun.
   When the enemy comes, of course I run,
   For I'm not cut out for the Army.
   When I left home, mamma, she cried;
   Mamma, she cried; mamma, she cried.
   When I left home, mamma, she cried,
   "He's not cut out for the Army."
   Refrain

3. The first time I went out for drill
   The bugler sounding made me ill.
   Of the battlefield, I'd had my fill,
   For I'm not cut out for the Army.
   The officers, they all did shout;
   All did shout; All did shout.
   The officers, they all did shout,
   "Why! Kick him out of the Army."
   Refrain

VIGOLIN

This tune is from a "Niederdeutsches" folk song, "Jan Hinnerk." The text is new, but hopefully, in the folk tradition.

STRUM: IA

GERMANY

Eng. version by Marilyn Keith
and Alan Bergman
Arr. by N. L.

Moderately ($\downarrow$ = 76)

234

1. There once was a man and he had a vi - o - lin, and he played his vi - o - lin where ev - er he did go. Where ev - er he did go, un - der - neath his dou - ble chin was his lit - tle vi - o -

2. Now no - bod - y knows that the lit - tle vi - o - lin, is a ma - gic vi - o - lin. No, no - one knows but he. No, no - one knows but he that the lit - tle vi - o - lin is a ma - gic vi - o -

235

BLOW AWAY THE MORNING DEW

The moral of this lively song is "A bird in the hand, etc." The first written record of this "escape" song is in 1719—one of the "Pills to Purge Melancholy."

STRUM: VIIIA

ENGLAND

Arr. by N. L.

Rhythmically—not too fast (♩ =104)

There was a knight, and he was young, Ri-ding on the way; And

there he met a la-dy fair, A - mong the ricks of hay. Sing-ing,

a tempo

Blow a - way the morn-ing dew, The dew and the dew.

Blow a - way the morn ing dew, How sweet the wind doth blow.

236

2. Quoth he, "Shall you and I, lady,
   Among the grass sit down?
   And I will have a special care
   For the rumpling of your gown." Singing,
   Refrain:

3. "Sir, if you'll go along with me
   Unto my father's hall,
   There you may have thrice kisses three,
   And my estate and all." Singing,
   Refrain:

4. He helped her to her snow white steed,
   He mounted on the other
   And then they rid along the road,
   Like sister and like brother. Singing,
   Refrain:

5. And when they reached her father's gate,
   So quickly she popped in.
   "Poof, you're a fool without," she said,
   "And I'm a maid within." Singing,
   Refrain:

6. "And if you meet a lady gay
   As you pass by yonder hill,
   If you will not when you may,
   You shall not when you will." Singing,
   Refrain:

237

VII

Sev'n for the sev'n stars in the sky, Six for the six proud walk-ers,
Five for the sym-bols at your door, Four for the gos-pel ma-kers,

VIII

Eight for the A-pril rain-ers,

Sev'n for the sev'n stars in the sky, Six for the six proud walk-ers,
Five for the sym-bols at your door, Four for the gos-pel mak-ers,

IX *sing three times*

Nine for the nine white shin-ers, Eight for the A-pril rain-ers,
Sev'n for the sev'n stars in the sky, Six for the six proud walk-ers,
Five for the sym-bols at your door, Four for the gos-pel mak-ers,

X

Ten for the Ten Com-mand-ments,

sing three times

Nine for the nine white shin-ers, Eight for the A-pril rain-ers,
Sev'n for the sev'n stars in the sky, Six for the six proud walk-ers,
Five for the sym-bols at your door, Four for the gos-pel mak-ers,

XI *sing four times*

'Lev'n for the 'lev'n that went to Heav'n, Ten for the Ten Com-mand-ments,
Nine for the nine white shin-ers, Eight for the A-pril rain-ers,
Sev'n for the sev'n stars in the sky, Six for the six proud walk-ers,
Five for the sym-bols at your door, Four for the gos-pel mak-ers,

XII

Twelve for the twelve a-pos-tles

sing four times

'Lev'n for the 'lev'n that went to Heav'n, Ten for the Ten Com-mand-ments,
Nine for the nine white shin-ers, Eight for the A-pril rain-ers,
Sev'n for the sev'n stars in the sky, Six for the six proud walk-ers,
Five for the sym-bols at your door, Four for the gos-pel mak-ers,

THE RAKES OF MALLOW

This tune is much better known than the words. Early eighteenth century Irish.

STRUM: IA

IRELAND

Arr. by N. L.

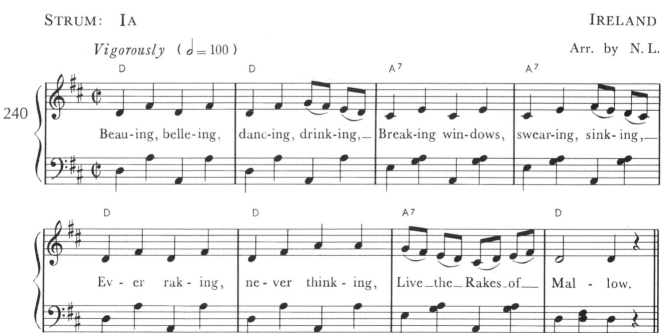

Vigorously (♩ = 100)

240

Beau-ing, belle-ing, danc-ing, drink-ing,— Break-ing win-dows, swear-ing, sink-ing,—

Ev-er rak-ing, ne-ver think-ing, Live_the_Rakes_of__ Mal-low.

Spend-ing—fast-er than it comes, Beat-ing—wait-ers, bai-liffs, duns. Bac-chus'—true be-got—ten sons, Live—the—Rakes—of— Mal - low.

2. One time nought but claret drinking,
   Then like politicians, thinking,
   Raising funds when funds are sinking.
   Live the rakes of Mallow.
   Living short but merry lives,
   Going where the Devil drives,
   Having sweethearts, but no wives,
   Live the rakes of Mallow.

3. Racking tenants, stewards teasing,
   Swiftly spending, slowly raising,
   Wishing thus to spend their days in
   Raking, as at Mallow.
   Then, to end this raking life,
   They get sober, take a wife,
   Ever after live in strife,
   Wishing e'er for Mallow.

241

ILKLEY MOOR BAHT HAT

This is a ballad from the North of England. "Baht hat" means without hat.

STRUM: VIII-A

ENGLAND

Arr. by N. L.

Vigorously - Not too slow (♩=120)

Verse

Where hast thou been since I saw thee, I saw thee? On
Il - kley Moor baht hat; ___ Where hast thou been since I saw
thee? Where hast thou been since I saw thee?
Where hast thou been since I saw thee?

Refrain

thee? On Il - kley Moor baht hat, baht hat, on
Where hast thou been since I saw thee? baht hat, on

242

Il - kley Moor baht hat, on Il - kley Moor baht hat.
Il - kley Moor baht hat, on Il - kley Moor baht ___ hat.

(♪)	♩	♩	♩	♩	♩	♩	♩	♩(♪)

2.　　I've　　been a —　court-in'　Ma — ry　Jane,　Ma — ry　Jane.....
On　Il — kley　Moor　baht　hat, *etc.*

3.　　There　wilt thou　catch thy　death of　cold,　death of　cold . . . . .
On　Il — kley　Moor　baht　hat, *etc.*

4.　　Then　we will　come and　bur — y　thee,　bur — y　thee . . . . .
On　Il — kley　Moor　baht　hat, *etc.*

5.　　Then　worms will　come and　eat thee　up,　eat thee　up . . . . . .
On　Il — kley　Moor　baht　hat, *etc.*

6.　　Then　ducks will　come and　eat up　worms,　eat up　worms . . .
On　Il — kley　Moor　baht　hat, *etc.*

7.　　Then　we will　come and　eat up　ducks,　eat up　ducks . . .
On　Il — kley　Moor　baht　hat, *etc.*

8.　　Then　us will　all have　et up　thee,　et up　thee . . . . .
On　Il — kley　Moor　baht　hat, *etc.*

243

EVERYBODY LOVES SATURDAY NIGHT

A joyful song with no particular message. Because "everybody loves Saturday night," we've included lyrics in many languages.

STRUM: IA or VIIIA

NIGERIA

Arr. by N. L.

Moderately fast; with a swing (♩ =100)

Ev'-ry-bo-dy loves Sat-ur-day night. ___
Bo-bo wa-ro fe-ro Sa - to - deh. ___

Ev'-ry-bo-dy, ev'-ry-bo-dy, ev'-ry-bo-dy, ev'-ry-bo-dy,
Bo-bo wa-ro, bo-bo wa-ro, bo-bo wa-ro, bo-bo wa-ro,

Ev'-ry-bo-dy loves Sat-ur-day night. ___
Bo-bo wa-ro fe-ro Sa - to - deh. ___

244

French: Tout le monde aime Samedi soir.
Yiddish: Jeder eyne hot lieb Shabas ba nacht.
Russian: Vsiem nravitsa Sabota vietcheram.
Ukrainian: Kozhdi lubit Subotu vechir.
Czech: Kazhdi ma rad Sabotu vietcher.
Polish: Kazdy lubi Soboty wieczur.
German: Jedermann liebt Samstag Abend.
Spanish: Todo el mundo le gusta la noche del Sábado.
Japanese: Dare demo doyobi ga suki.
Chinese: Ren ren shi huan li pei lu.
Hebrew: Kol echad ohev Shabat ba laila.
Hawaiian: Ke puni kela mea i Po'aono po.

This is
sometimes sung
as a children's
play song
in the
Cajun country.

STRUM: IA

UNITED STATES

Arr. by N. L.

Lively (♩ = 108)

Verse

One, two, three, Ca-ro-line, turn your-self like this, my dear;
Un, deux, trois, Ca-ro-line, qui fais com-me ça, ma chêre.

One, two, three, Ca-ro-line, turn your-self like that, my dear.
Un, deu trois, Ca-ro-line, qui fais com-me ça, ma chêre.

STRUM: IC

Refrain (♩ = ♩.)

Ma-ma says yes, Pa-pa says no. Which way to turn, which way to go?
Ma-man dit oui, pa-pa dit non ce-lui mo lais, ce-lui mo prends?

Ma-ma says yes, Pa-pa says no. What should I do, how should I know?
Ma-man dit oui, Pa-pa dit non, ce-lui mo lais, ce-lui mo prends?

245

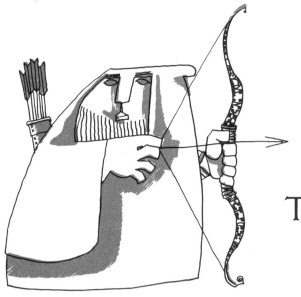

THE KEEPER WOULD
A-HUNTING GO

A question and answer song, known in almost identical forms
both in England and in the United States.

STRUM: IA

ENGLAND
Arr. by N.L.

Lively (♩=184)

Verse

The keep-er would a hunt-ing go, And un-der his coat he car-ried a bow,

All for to shoot at the mer-ry lit-tle doe, A-mong the leaves so green, O.

Refrain

*I II I II I II

Jack-ie boy! Mas-ter? Sing ye well? Ve-ry well. Hey down! Ho down!

I All I

Der-ry der-ry down! A-mong the leaves so green, O. To my

246

*Voices should divide into two groups at refrain, singing as indicated by I (group one), II (group two),
or All (together).

hey, down, down! To my ho, down, down! Hey down! Ho down! Der - ry der - ry down. A - mong the leaves so green, O!

2. The	The first	doe	he	shot	at	he	missed......
	The sec — ond	one	he	at	trimmed	and	kissed.......
	The third	one	went	where	no —	body	wist,.......
	A — mong	the	leaves	so	green,	O!...........
Refrain:							

3. The	The fourth	doe,	she	did	cross	the	plain........
	The keep — er	she	fetched	her	back	a —	gain..........
	Where she is	now	she	may	re —	main,......
	A — mong	the	leaves	so	green,	O!...........
Refrain:							

247

4. The	The fifth	doe,	she	did	cross	the	brook......
	The keep — er	she	fetched	her	back	with his	crook......
	Where she is	now,	you	must	go	look,.......
	A — mong	the	leaves	so	green,	O!.............
Refrain:							

5. The	The sixth	doe	she	ran	o —	ver the	plain,......
	But he	with his	hounds	did	turn	her a —	gain,
And it's	there	he did	hunt	in a	mer-ry,	mer-ry	vein,.......
	A — mong	the	leaves	so	green,	O!..........
Refrain:							

I'VE GOT NO USE
FOR THE WOMEN

This tune is too robust and vital for this misogynic cowboy's message to ring true.
(Most enjoyable when sung by men within the hearing of women.)

STRUM: I-B

UNITED STATES

Arr. by N. L.

Not too fast (♩ =160)

248

I've got no use for the wo-men; _____ A
true one can nev-er be found. _____ They'll
use a man for his mo-ney; _____ When it's
gone they'll turn him down. _____

They're all a-like at the bot-tom, _____ Self-ish and grasp-ing for all. _____ They'll stick with a man when he's win-ning, _____ And laugh in his face at his fall. _____

2. My   pal was an honest cowpuncher,
             Honest and upright and true;
   But he   turned to a hardshooting gunman,
   On ac-   count of a girl named Lou.
   He   fell in with evil companions,
   The   kind that are better off dead;
   When a   gambler insulted her picture,
   He   filled him full of lead.

3.   All thru the long night they trailed him,
   Thru   mesquite and thick chaparral;
   And I   couldn't help think of that woman
   As I   saw him pitch and fall.
   If   she'd been the pal that she should have,
   He   might have been raising a son,
   In-   stead of out there on the prairie,
   To   die by a ranger's gun.

4.   Death's dark fears did not trouble.
   His   chances of life were too slim;
   But   where they are putting his body
   Was   all that worried him.
   He   raised himself on his elbow.
   The   blood from his wounds flowed red.
   He   gazed at his pals all around him,
   And   these are the words that he said,

5.   "Bury me out on the prairie,
   Where the coyotes can howl o'er my grave;
             Bury me out on the prairie,
   But from them my bones please save.
             Wrap me up in my blanket,
   And   bury me deep in the ground;
             Cover me over with boulders
   Of   granite grey and round."

6. So we   buried him out on the prairie,
   Where the coyotes can howl o'er his grave;
   And his   soul is now a-resting,
   From the unkind cut she gave.
   And   many another puncher,
   As he   rides past that pile of stones,
   Re-   calls some similar woman
   And   thinks of his own mouldrin' bones.

K E M O K I M O

Sheer nonsense set to a wonderful, lively melody from the Kentucky mountains.

STRUM: Ia

UNITED STATES

Arr. by N. L.

Lively (♩ = 104)

In Car-o-li-na the folks all go, Sing song kit-ty, can't you ki-me-oh?

There's where the folks all plant the tow, Sing song kit-ty, can't you ki-me-oh?

Cov-er the ground all o-ver with smoke, Sing song kit-ty, can't you ki-me-oh?

250

Then their heads a-round they poke, Sing song kit-ty, can't you ki-me-oh?

Refrain

Ke-mo ki-mo, there, oh where? With my hi, my ho, and in come Sal-ly, singin'

Some-time pen-ny wink-le ling-tum nip-cat, Sing song kit-ty, can't you ki-me-oh?

(similarly)

251

2. Oh, what you gonna do when the rain don't fall?
Sing song kitty, can't you ki-me-o?
Crops grow small instead of tall.
Sing song kitty, *etc.*
Ev'ry thing seems to turn out wrong.
Sing song kitty, *etc.*
Cotton's short instead of long.
Sing song kitty, *etc.*
Refrain

3. There was a frog lived in a pool.
Sing song kitty, can't you ki-me-o?
Sure he was the biggest fool.
Sing song kitty, *etc.*
He could dance and he could sing.
Sing song kitty, *etc.*
Make the woods aroun' him ring.
Sing song kitty, *etc.*
Refrain

OLD DAN TUCKER

A song
of the frontier days
with not too much logic,
but great fun.

STRUM: Ia

UNITED STATES

Arr. by N. L.

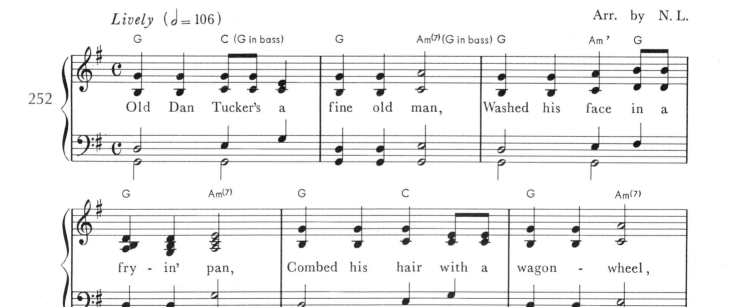

Lively (♩ = 106)

252

Old Dan Tucker's a fine old man, Washed his face in a fry-in' pan, Combed his hair with a wagon-wheel,

2. I   come to town the other night,
To   hear the noise and see the fight.
The   watchman he was a-runnin' around,
Cryin' "Old Dan Tucker's come to town".
Refrain

3.   Old Dan Tucker come to town,
Riding a billygoat, leading a hound.
Hound, he barked, the billygoat jumped,
Throwed Dan straddle of a stump.
Refrain

4.   Old Dan Tucker clumb a tree,
His   Lord and Master for to see.
The   limb, it broke, Dan got a fall,
Never got to see his Lord at all.
Refrain

5.   Old Dan Tucker, he got drunk.
Fell in the fire and he kicked up a chunk.
Red hot coal got in his shoe;
Lord Godamighty, how the ashes flew!
Refrain

6.   Old Dan Tucker, he came to town,
Swinging the ladies 'round and 'round.
First to the right and then to the left,
And   then to the one that you love best.
Refrain

7. Old   Dan and me, we did fall out,
And   what do you reckon it was about?
He   stepped on my corn, I kicked him on the shin,
And   that's the way this row begin.
Refrain

253

A CAPITAL SHIP

This is a parody of life at sea. Not really a folk song but certainly a joy for folk to sing.

STRUM: I-A

ENGLAND

Arr. by N. L.

Lively (♩ = 100)

Verse

A cap-i-tal ship for an o-cean trip Was the "Wal-lop-ing Win-dow Blind." No wind that blew dis-mayed her crew Or trou-bled the cap-tain's mind. The man at the wheel was made to feel Con-tempt for the wild-est blow-ow-ow, Tho' it oft ap-pear'd when the gale had clear'd That he'd been in his bunk be-low.

254

Refrain

So, blow, ye winds, heigh-ho, A-rov-ing I will go; I'll
stay no more on Eng-land's shore, So let the mu-sic play-ay-ay; I'm

a tempo

off for the morn-ing train, I'll cross the rag-ing main, I'm
off to my love with a box-ing glove, Ten thous-and miles a-way.

2. The bo'sun's mate was very sedate,
   Yet fond of amusement, too.
   He played hop-scotch with the starboard watch,
   While the captain tickled the crew.
   The gunner we had was apparently mad,
   For he sat on the after ra-ai-ail,
   And fired salutes with the captain's boots
   In the teeth of a booming gale.
   Refrain

3. The captain sat on the commodore's hat,
   And dined in a royal way
   Off pickles and figs, and little roast pigs,
   And gunnery bread each day.
   The cook was Dutch and behaved as such,
   For the diet he served the crew-ew-ew
   Was a couple of tons of hot-cross buns
   Served up with sugar and glue.
   Refrain

4. Then we all fell ill as mariners will
   On a diet that's rough and crude;
   And we shivered and shook as we dipped the cook
   In a tub of his gluesome food.
   All nautical pride we cast aside,
   And we ran the vessel asho-o-ore
   On the Gulliby Isles, where the poopoo smiles,
   And the rubbily ubdugs roar.
   Refrain

5. Composed of sand was that favored land,
   And trimmed with cinnamon straws,
   And pink and blue was the pleasing hue
   Of the tickle-toe-teaser's claws.
256
   We sat on the edge of a sandy ledge,
   And shot at the whistling bee-ee-ee,
   While the ring-tailed bats wore waterproof hats
   As they dipped in the shining sea.
   Refrain

6. On rugbug bark from dawn till dark
   We dined till we all had grown
   Uncommonly shrunk, when a Chinese junk
   Came up from the Torrible Zone.
   She was chubby and square, but we didn't much care,
   So we cheerily put to sea-ee-ea,
   And we left all the crew of the junk to chew
   On the bark of the rugbug tree.
   Refrain

WELL-LOVED PLACES

THE BLAYDON RACES

Arr. by N. L.

STRUM: I-A

ENGLAND

New
this comic account of an essentially local affai
had amazingly wide popularity for over 100

Lively (♩=120)

Verse

Aa went to Blay - don ra - ces, 'twas on the ninth of June, Eight - teen hun - dred and six - ty two, on a sum - mer's af - ter - noon. Aa tyuk the bus fra' Balm - bra's, and she was heav - y lad - en. A - way we went a - lang Coll - ing - wood street that's on the road to Blay - don.

Refrain

Oh,_____ ma lads! Ya shud - a seen us gan - in',

258

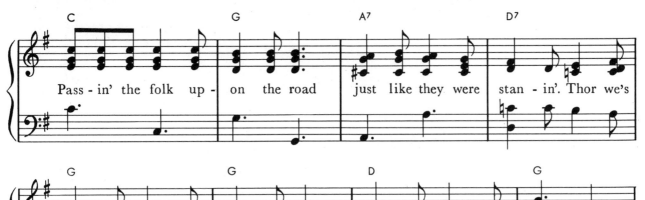

Pass-in' the folk up-on the road | just like they were | stan-in'. Thor we's

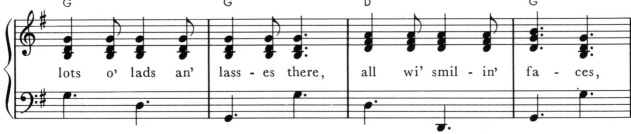

lots o' lads an' | lass-es there, | all wi' smil-in' | fa - ces,

Gan-nin' a-lang the | Scots-wood road, to | see the Blay-don | ra - ces.

2. We flew past Armstrong's factory
   And up to "Robin Adair",
   Just gannin' doon to the railway bridge.
   The bus wheel flew off there;
   The lasses lost thor crinolines
   An' the veils that hide thor faces;
   Aa got two black eyes an' a broken nose
   In ga'n to Blaydon Races.
   Refrain:

3. When we gat the wheel put on,
   Away we went agyen,
   But them that had their noses broke,
   They cam' back ower hyem.
   Sum went to the dispensary,
   An' sum to Doctor Gibbs,
   An' sum to the informary
   To mend their broken ribs.
   Refrain:

4. Noo, when we gat to Paradise,
   Thor wes bonny gams begun.
   Thor wes fower an' twenty on the bus;
   Man, hoo they danc'd and sung.
   They caal'd on me to sing a song
   Aa sang them "Paddy Fagen";
   Aa danc'd a jig an' swung me twig
   That day aa went to Blaydon.
   Refrain:

5. We flew across the Chine Bridge
   Reet intiv Blaydon Toon.
   The bellman, he was callin' there;
   They call'd him Jacky Broon;
   Aa saa him taakin' to sum chaps,
   An' them he was persuadin'
   Te gan an' see Geordy Ridley's show
   In the Mechanics Hall at Blaydon.
   Refrain:

6. The rain it poored a' the day
   An' mayed the groonds quite muddy.
   Coffy Johnny had a white hat on.
   They yelled, "Who stole the cuddy?"
   Thor wes spice stalls an' monkey shows,
   An' ald wives sellin' ciders,
   An' a chap wi' a ha'penny roondaboot
   Shootin', "Noo, me lads," for riders.
   Refrain:

259

Derived from the Texas song, "Brazos River," this has had all its landmarks moved to the state of "Elanoy."

DOWN BY THE EMBARRAS

STRUM: I-B

UNITED STATES

Arr. by N. L.
New words by W.S.

Moderately, with a swing (♩=152)

Verse

I've crossed the *Des - plaines and I've ford - ed the Ver - mil - lion. I've

swum the Lit - tle Wa - bash, I've fol - lowed the Ap - ple. The

Cal - u - met's mud - dy, the Rock Ri - ver clear, But

down by the *Em - barras I court - ed my dear.

260

Refrain

Li - la - li lee lee lee, give me your hand,

Li - la - li lee lee lee, give me your hand.

Li - la - li lee lee lee, give me your hand, There's

man-y a riv - er that wa - ters the land.

* Pronunciations:
Embarras = Ahm—brah
Desplaines = Des—plainz
Macaupin = Ma—koo—pin

2. The broad Illinois, it runs glossy and gliding.
The crooked Kaskaskia runs weaving and winding.
Old Abe Lincoln's Sangamon, it courses the plain,
And I never will walk by the Embarras again.
Refrain

3. She hugged me, she kissed me, she called me her dandy.
The Mackinaw's rocky, the Kankakee sandy.
She kissed me, she hugged me, she called me her own,
But down by the Embarras, she left me alone.
Refrain

4. The girls of the Fox, O, they're plump and they're pretty.
The Spoon and *Macaupin have many a beauty.
The Chicago flows slowly past girls by the score,
So down by the Embarras, I'll wander no more.
Refrain

261

BEYOND THE MOUNTAINS

A song of great longing for the outside world, yet regret in leaving home—the most "well-loved place."

SWITZERLAND
English lyrics by
Marilyn Keith
and Alan Bergman
Arr. by N. L.

STRUM: IIIB or IIB

Warmly (♩ = 60)

Verse

There lies a world be-yond the moun-tains, There lies a world for me to see. And I must go be-yond the moun-tains. And leave the home so dear to me.

Refrain

La la la la la la la la la, la la la la la la la la, And I must go be-yond the moun-tains and ___ leave the home so dear to me.

262

2. My father lived beneath the mountains,
   As did his father long ago,
   And I was born beneath the mountains.
   They are the only home I know.
   La-la-la-la-la-la-la-la-la, (*twice*)
   And I was born, *etc*.

3. And so, farewell, O friendly mountains.
   The time has come for me to roam,
   And e'er I go beyond the mountains,
   I know my heart will long for home.
   La-la-la-la-la-la-la-la-la, (*twice*)
   And e'er I go, *etc*.

263

FAREWELL TO LIVERPOOL

A forecastle shanty of great warmth and nostalgia.

STRUM: IIA

ENGLAND - IRELAND

Arr. by N. L.

With movement - not too slow (♩=72)

Verse

Fare - well to Prin - ce's — Land - ing Stage, Riv - er
Mer - sey, fare thee well; I am bound for Cal - i -
for - nee - o, A place — I know quite well.

264

Refrain

So fare thee well, my own true love. When I re-turn, u-ni-ted we will be. It's not the leav-ing of Liv-er-pool that grieves me, But, my dar-ling, when I think of thee.

2. I have shipp'd on board a clip — per ship,
Da — vy Crock — ett is her name;.................
And the cap — tain of her is Bur — gess,
And they say she's a float — ing shame.................
Refrain:

3. I am bound for Cal — i — for — nee – o,
By way of stormy Cape Horn.................
And I'll write to you a let — ter,
When I am home — ward bound.................
Refrain:

4. I have shipp'd a — gain with Bur — gess,
And I think I know him well.................
If a man's a sail — or he will get a — long; ..
If not he will live in Hell.................
Refrain:

5. Fare — well to Low — er Fred — rick Street,
Hand- some Ter — race, and Park Lane;.................
For I know it will be a long, long time,
Till I re — turn a — gain.................
Refrain:

265

HAL FAR BISS

"Hal Far Biss" was an R.A.F. airfield on Malta, under constant siege from 1940-1943. The tune is the Welsh folk song "All Through the Night."

STRUM: IX

ENGLAND

Arr. by N. L.

Freely Not too slow (♩=88)

(Chorus) What's the proud-est 'drome in Mal-ta? Hal Far Biss.

One the Ax-is could not al-ter; Hal Far Biss.

266

'Neath the weight of mines it's quak-ing, Bomb blasts o'er it ra-di-a-ting;

But it's al-ways op-er-a-ting, Hal Far Biss.

2. See them rounding Delimara,
   Hal Far Biss.
   'Cross the bay to Kalaframa,
   Hal Far Biss.
   Stukas dropping thousand pounders,
   ME's strafing all around us,
   Take three guesses where they found us,
   Hal Far Biss.

3. When we leave and go to Blighty,
   Hal Far Biss.
   We shall ne'er forget the mighty
   Hal Far Biss.
   Thru the blitzes we preserv'd it,
   And we're proud that we have serv'd it.
   Malta's George Cross, who deserv'd it?
   Hal Far Biss.

O, VERMELAND

One of the most beautiful of all folk tunes dating back to the seventeenth century. The poet, A. Fryxell, set his text, "Ach, Värmeland, du Sköna," around 1850.

STRUM: IX

SWEDEN

Eng. Version by W.S.
Arr. by N.L.

Freely (♩ = 96)

O Ver - me -land, my heart cries in long - ing from a - far For
Ack, Vär - me - land, du skö - na, du här - li - ga land, Du

thee, O, most pre - cious spot in Swe - den. Though
kro - na bland Sve - a - ri - kes län - der. Ock

268

years have past since I've been gone, you're still my guid - ing star, The
kom - me jag än midt i det för - löf - va - de land, Till

2. O Vermeland, pray tell, is my true love waiting still,
And has she kept the promise that was spoken?
Tell her that I'll be faithful to both you and her, until
The cruel ties that keep me here are broken.
For you and her I live, and for you and her I'd die.
And if, in mercy, God will but let me come back home,
I'll gladly forswear all hope of heaven.

2. Ja, när du en gång skall bort och gifta dig, min vän,
Då skall du till Värmeland fara.
Där finnes nog Guds gåfvor af flickor kvar igen,
Och alla ä' de präktiga och rara.
Men friar du där, så var munter och glad,
Ty raska gossar vilja Värmelandsflickorna ha,
De sorgsna dem ge de uppå båten.

THE ROAD TO THE ISLES

A vigorous yet tender tune from the Hebrides.

STRUM: IX-A

SCOTLAND (Hebrides)

Rhythmically, moderately fast (♩=120)

Arr. by N. L.

270

Oh, a far croon-in is pull-in' me a-way As take I wi' my cro-mak to the road. Oh, the far cool-ins are put-tin' love on me As step I wi' the sun-light for my load.

Refrain

Sure, by Tum-mel and Loch Ran-noch and Loch A - ber I will go, By heath - er tracks wi' heav - en in their wiles; If it's think - in' in your in-ner heart the brag-gart's in my step, You've nev - er smelt the tang - le o' the isles. Oh, the far cool - ins are put - tin' love on me, As step I wi' my cro-mak to the isles.

271

2. It's by Sheil* water the track is to the west,
   By Aillort† and by Morar to the sea,
   The cool cresses I am thinkin' o' for pluck,
   And bracken for a wink on mother's knee.
   Refrain

3. It's the blue islands are pullin' me away,
   Their laughter puts the leap upon the lame;
   The blue islands from the Skerries to the Lews,°
   Wi' heather honey taste upon each name.
   Refrain

* Sheil, pronounced "sheel"
† Aillort, pronounce first syllable as "isle"
° Lews, pronounced "lose"

MEADOWLAND

This song became well-known during World War II because it symbolized the
heroic struggle of the Russians against the invaders.

STRUM: IA

U. S. S. R.

Eng. version
and
Arr. by N. L.

Steadily (♩ = 120)

Mea - dow - land, mea - dow - land,

Mea - dows green and full of blos - som;

Mea - dows which our fath - ers have held dear be - fore us;

Mea - dows which our sons will love to - mor - row.

2. Meadowland, meadowland,
   History tells a bloody story.
   Long were your hills and valleys torn and ravaged,
   Long were you oppressed by the invader.

3. Meadowland, meadowland,
   Now the storm has pass'd behind us.
   May we live in peace and hope for now and ever,
   May we live in peace and hope forever.
   Repeat verse 1.

THE CUP THAT CHEERS

LIFT A GLASS

Manufactured from a fragment, this song is certainly in the tradition of cumulative folk songs.

STRUM: IA

POLAND
English lyrics by Marilyn Keith
and Alan Bergman
Arr. by N. L.

Lively (♩ = 104)

Verse

Ya-cob drinks with farm-er Fred-'rick, Fill the friend-ly glass-es.

Mi-chael drinks with May-or Drob-ny, How the even-ing pass-es.

Refrain

Now we lift our glass-es high, Ya-cob, Fred-'rick, you and I!

Repeat as needed

Ya-cob drinks with farm-er Fred-'rick,
Mi-chael drinks with Ma-yor Drob-ny,
Wu-pu-tsu-pu, wu-pu-tsu-pu,
Lift a glass to friend-ship.

274

2. Lazlo drinks with Uncle Stefan, steins are overflowing!
   Peter drinks with Yan the baker, merriment is growing.
   Now we lift our glasses high, Lazlo, Stefan, you and I!
   Yacob drinks with farmer Fred'rick,
   Michael drinks with Mayor Drobny,
   Lazlo drinks with Uncle Stefan,
   Peter drinks with Yan the baker.
   Wu pu tsu pu, wu pu tsu pu, lift a glass to friendship!

3. Very soon the purse is empty, how the evening passes!
   Now we toast the kindly barman, kindly fill the glasses!
   Now we lift our glasses high, kindly barman, you and I!
   Yacob drinks with farmer Fred'rick,
   Michael drinks with Mayor Drobny,
   Lazlo drinks with Uncle Stefan,
   Peter drinks with Yan the baker.
   Kindly barman, fill the glasses!
   How the evening quickly passes.
   Wu pu tsu, pu, wu pu tsu pu, lift a glass to friendship!

A WEE DRAPPIE O'T

This is to be sung slowly, with deference to the convivial inertia of a group that has been enjoying each others company and "a wee drappie o't."

STRUM: IX or IA

SCOTLAND

Freely (♩=138)

Arr. by N. L.

Verse

(Chorus) This life is a jour-ney___ we all hae to gang, And

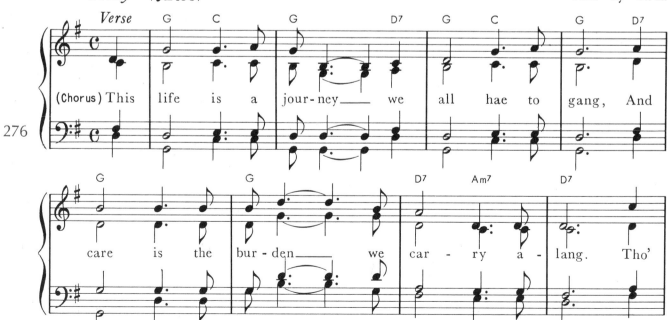

care is the bur-den___ we car-ry a-lang. Tho'

276

heav-y be our bur-den and pov-er-ty our lot, We'll be
hap-py a' - the - gi -ther o'er a wee drap-pie o't.

Refrain

O'er a wee drap-pie o't, o'er a wee drap-pie o't, We'll be
hap-py a' - the - gi - ther o'er a wee drap-pie o't.

277

2. The trees are a' stripp'd o' their mantles sea green,
   The leaves o' the forest nae langer are seen.
   For winter is here wi' its cold icy coat,
   And we're all met the-gith-er o'er a wee drappie o't.

Refrain:

   O'er a wee drappie o't, o'er a wee drappie o't,
   And we're all met the-gith-er o'er a wee drappie o't.

3. Job in his lamentations said that man was made to mourn,
   And there's nae such thing as pleasures from the cradle to the urn;
   But in his lamentations he surely had forgot
   A' the pleasure man enjoys o'er a wee drappie o't.

Refrain:

   O'er a wee drappie o't, o'er a wee drappie o't,
   A' the pleasure man enjoys o'er a wee drappie o't.

THE THREE TAILORS

A lively ballad with a moral similar to the "escape" songs.

GERMANY

Eng. Version by W.S.

Arr. by N.L.

STRUM: IX

Freely (♩.= 54)

Three tai-lors once walked to the banks of the Rhine, And they stopped at a tav-ern in old In-gle-heim, On the Rhine, on the Rhine. They had-n't a pen-ny a-mong the three, But each was as thirst-y as

Es ka-men drei Schei-der wohl an den Rhien, Und kehr-ten beim Gast-wirth zu In-gel-heim ein, Am Rhein, am Rhein. Sie hat-ten im Sack kei-nen Hel-ler mehr, Doch dur-ste-te Je-dem von

278

thirst-y can be For___ wine,_____ for___ wine._____
ih - nen sehr Nach___ Wein,_____ nach___ Wein._____

2. "Good landlord, it happens we're fresh out of cash,
   Even though in our trade we all cut quite a dash
   On the Rhine, on the Rhine.
   We'll each of us show you the tricks of our craft,
   If you, in exchange, will give us a draft
   Of wine, of wine."

3. "You're on!" said the landlord of old Ingleheim.
   "If your tricks do impress me, I'll draw you some wine
   On the Rhine, on the Rhine.
   But if your boast's merely the product of thirst,
   I'll pitch you all into the river head first,
   'Stead of wine, 'stead of wine."

4. The first tailor grasped a thin strand of sunlight,
   And with it he threaded his needle so bright
   On the Rhine, on the Rhine.
   He sewed up an old broken wine glass; 'twas neat,
   For you hardly could tell where the seams did meet
   For wine, for wine.

5. The first tailor sat, and the second arose,
   And picked a fat flea off the landlord's red nose,
   On the Rhine, on the Rhine.
   The poor little beast had a hole in his sock.
   'Twas fixed in exactly one tick of the clock
   For wine, for wine.

6. "Watch this," said the third, "You've seen nothing at all",
   And he drove his long needle far into the wall
   On the Rhine, on the Rhine.
   He flew back and forth through the needle's eye.
   If it isn't the truth, then I hope I may die
   From wine, from wine.

279

7. Said the landlord, "My boys, to your promise you're true.
   My bargain I'll keep, but I have some tricks, too.
   On the Rhine, on the Rhine."
   He filled up three thimbles with wine clear and bright.
   "Drink hearty, magicians, let's see you get tight!
   There's your wine, there's your wine!"

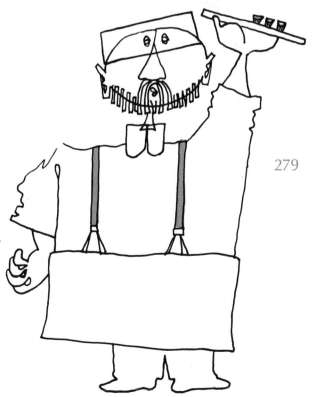

WHISKEY JOHNNY!

Halyard shanties were used mainly for longer pulls. This is one of the oldest. It is also a reminder to the skipper that a long pull of grog would not be amiss.

STRUM: Ia

BRITISH ISLES
and
NORTH AMERICA

Arr. by N. L.

Lively ($\downarrow = 96$)

O, whis - key is the life of man.

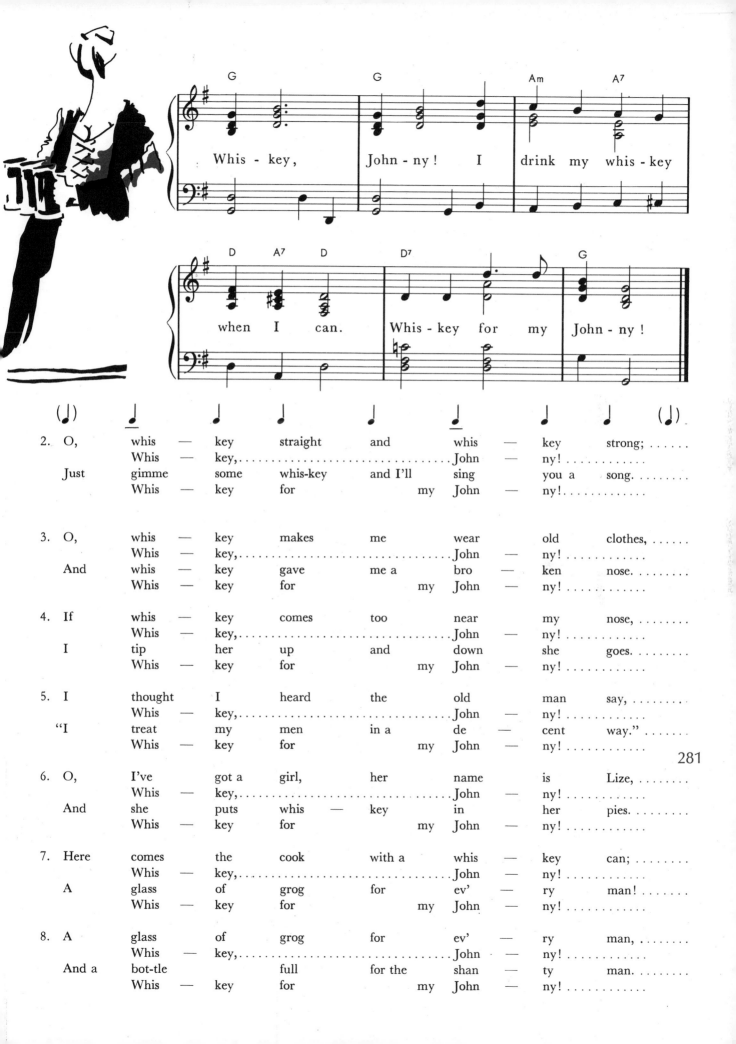

Whis - key, | John - ny ! | I | drink my whis - key

when I can. | Whis - key for my | John - ny !

(♩)   ♩   ♩   ♩   ♩   ♩   ♩   ♩   (♩)

2. O, whis — key straight and whis — key strong; . . . . . .
    Whis — key, ... John — ny ! . . . .
   Just gimme some whis-key and I'll sing you a song. . . . .
    Whis — key for my John — ny ! . . . .

3. O, whis — key makes me wear old clothes, ...
    Whis — key, ... John — ny ! . . . .
   And whis — key gave me a bro — ken nose. . . . .
    Whis — key for my John — ny ! . . . .

4. If whis — key comes too near my nose, ...
    Whis — key, ... John — ny ! . . . .
   I tip her up and down she goes. . . . .
    Whis — key for my John — ny ! . . . .

5. I thought I heard the old man say, ...
    Whis — key, ... John — ny ! . . . .
  "I treat my men in a de — cent way." . . . . . .
    Whis — key for my John — ny ! . . . .

281

6. O, I've got a girl, her name is Lize, ...
    Whis — key, ... John — ny ! . . . .
  And she puts whis — key in her pies. . . . .
    Whis — key for my John — ny ! . . . .

7. Here comes the cook with a whis — key can; . . . .
    Whis — key, ... John — ny ! . . . .
  A glass of grog for ev' — ry man! . . . .
    Whis — key for my John — ny ! . . . .

8. A glass of grog for ev' — ry man, ...
    Whis — key, ... John — ny ! . . . .
  And a bot-tle full for the shan — ty man. . . . . . .
    Whis — key for my John — ny ! . . . .

THE WINE TESTERS

After a series of tastes to "see if the wine is good," this song gets better and better.

STRUM: IA+B

FRANCE

Eng. Version by W.S.
Arr. by N.L.

Gaily (♩ = 120)

Let us all gath-er round the ta-ble Just to see if the wine is good. Let us
Che-va-liers de la ta-ble ron-de, Gou-tons voir si le vin est bon. Che-va-

2. If it's clear, and it isn't cloudy,
   Let us taste of the wine that's good. } *twice*
   Let us taste, oui, oui, oui,
   Let use taste, non, non, non, } *twice*
   Let us taste of the wine that's good. }

(*similarly*)

3. Now we're sure, so let's raise our glasses, } *twice*
   And we'll drink of the wine that's good.
   And we'll drink, *etc.*

4. One good swallow deserves another. } *twice*
   Drink it down for the wine is good.
   Drink it down, *etc.*

5. Once we're started, there's no use stopping. } *twice*
   Bottoms up with the wine that's good.
   Bottoms up, *etc.*

6. Let's forget all about tomorrow. } *twice*
   Drink today while the wine is good.
   Drink today, *etc.*

7. Empty bottles deserve companions. } *twice*
   Drink some more of the wine that's good.
   Drink some more, *etc.*

2. S'il est bon, s'il est agréable,
   J'en boirai jusqu'a mon plaisir. } *twice*
   J'en boirai, oui, oui, oui,
   J'en boirai, non, non, non, } *twice*
   J'en boirai jusqu'a mon plaisir.

(*similarly*)

3. J'en boirai cinq ou six bouteilles,
   Une femme sur les genoux.

4. Toc, toc, toc, on frappe à la porte
   Je crois bien que c'est son mari.

5. Si c'est lui, que le diable l'emporte
   Car il vient troubler mon plaisir.

6. Si je meurs, je veux qu'on m'enterre
   Dans la cave où il y a du bon vin.

7. Et les quatre plus grands ivrognes
   Porteront les quat' coins du drap.

8. Les deux pied contre la muraille
   Et la tete sous le robinet.

9. Sur ma tombe je veux qu'on inscrive
   "Ici git le roi des bouvers."

10. La morale de cette histoire,
    C'est a boire avant de mourir.

A gang song, rather than a real folk song, but certainly a reflection of its time. Poking fun at the whole area of "patent medicine." (At one time Mrs. Pinkham's tonic was sixty proof, which entitles it to be in this category.)

STRUM: Ic

UNITED STATES

284

Spirited ($\downarrow$. = 112)

We will sing_____ of Ly-di-a Pink-ham,_____ And her

love_____ for the hu-man race._____ How she

sells_____ her veg'-ta-ble com-pound,_____ And the

pa - - pers, they pub-lish her face._____

Sing, — O, sing, O, sing, O, sing, of Ly-di - a Pink- ham, — And her love, her love, her love for the hu - man race. — How — she makes, she bot-tles, she sells her veg'-ta - ble com - pound, — And the pa - - - pers, they pub - lish her face. —

2. O, it sells for a dollar a bottle,
   And it cures all manner of ills.
   It is more to be recommended
   Than Carter's Liver Pills.
   Refrain:

3. O, she died and went to heaven,
   At the age of a hundred and eight.
   And she took some veg'table compound,
   So they'd let her in at the gate.
   Refrain:

4. Widow Brown, she had no children,
   Though she lov'd them very dear.
   So she took some veg'table compound,
   Now she has them twice a year.
   Refrain:

5. Take a swallow when you awaken,
   And your pains will disappear.
   Keep on taking it ev'ry hour,
   And by noon you'll switch to beer.
   Refrain:

VIVE LA COMPAGNIE

Despite the French title, this is an American song, and a great favorite with "boon companions."

STRUM: IVC or IC

UNITED STATES

Arr. by N. L.

Vigorously (♩.=88)

Verse

Solo — Let ev'ry good fel-low now fill up his glass, Vi-ve la com-pag-nie,— And

drink to the health of our glo-ri-ous class Vi-ve la com-pag-nie.

Refrain

Vi-ve la vi-ve la vi-ve l' amour, Vi-ve la, vi-ve la, vi-ve l' amour,

Vi-ve l' amour, vi-ve l' amour, Vi-ve la com-pag-nie.

286

2. Let ev'ry good married man drink to his wife;
   Vive la compagnie,
   The joy of his bosom, the plague of his life.
   Vive la compagnie.
   Refrain

3. Come, fill up your glasses; I'll give you a toast:
   Vive la compagnie.
   "Here's health to our friend, our kind, worthy host."
   Vive la compagnie.
   Refrain

4. Since all with good humor I've toasted so free,
   Vive la compagnie,
   I hope it will please you to drink now with me.
   Vive la compagnie.

GAUDEAMUS IGITUR

A universal drinking song of students everywhere, this is an eighteenth century German melody.

STRUM: IXB or IB

EUROPE
and
NORTH AMERICA

Moderately, with spirit ($\downarrow$=88)

Arr. by N. L.

2. Ubi sunt qui ante nos } twice
In mundo fuere?
Transeas ad superos
Abeas ad inferos,
Ques si vis videre,
Ques si vis videre.

3. Vivat academia, } twice
Vivat profesores.
Vivet membrum quodlibet,
Vivat membra quaelibet,
Semper sint in flore,
Semper sint in flore.

VALOR AND FREEDOM

THE THREE RAVENS

This song and the next two have much in common. This one is based on a Gregorian tune; a story of death and carrion.

STRUM: IX

ENGLAND

Arr. by N. L.

Freely (♩ = 104)

There were three rav-ens on a tree, Down-a-down, hey down-a-down. And they were black as black can be, With a down. The one of them said to his mate, "Where shall we our break-fast take?" With a down, der-ry, der-ry, der-ry, down, down.

290

(♩) ♩ ♩ ♩ ♩ ♩ ♩ ♩ (♪)

2. Down in yon — der green field, ...
   Down — a — down, hey down — a — down,
There lies a knight slain un-der his shield,
With a down. . . . .
His hounds they lie down at his feet,
So well can they their mas — ter keep.
With a down, der-ry, der-ry, der-ry, down, down. . . .

3. His hawks they fly so eag — er — ly, ...
   Down — a — down, hey down — a — down.
There is no fowl dare him come nigh.
With a down. . . . .
   Down there comes a fal — low doe,
As great with young as she might go.
With a down, der-ry, der-ry, der-ry, down, down. . . .

4. She lift — ed up his blood — y head, . . .
   Down — a — down, hey down — a — down,
And kiss'd the wounds that were so red,
With a down. . . . .
She got him up up — on her back,
And car — ried him to earth — en lake,
With a down, der-ry, der-ry, der-ry, down, down. . . .

5. She bur — ied him be — fore the prime, . . .
   Down — a — down, hey down — a — down.
She was dead her — self ere e — ven-song time,
With a down. . . . .
God send to ev' — ry gen — tle man
Such hawks, such hounds, and such a le — man.
With a down, der-ry, der-ry, der-ry, down, down. . . .

BILLY McGEE McGAW

The text is similar, but this is a variant of a tune better known as "When Johnny Comes Marching Home."

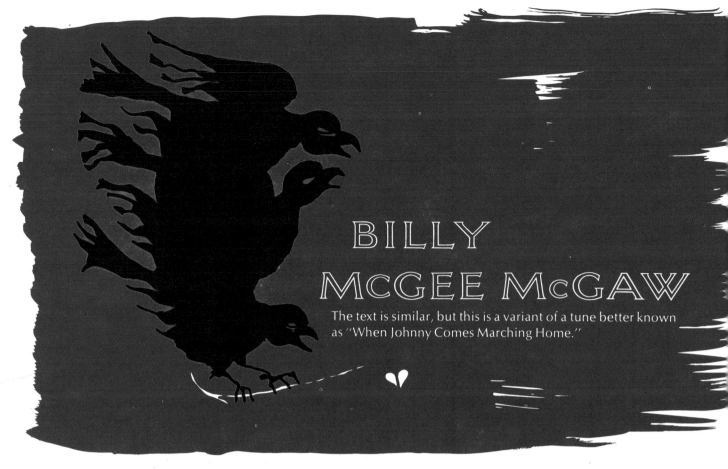

STRUM: IVc

UNITED STATES

Arr. by N. L.

Like a march (♩.=108)

There were three crows sat on a tree. Bil-ly Mc-Gee Mc-

Gaw._____ There were three crows sat on a tree. Oh,

Bil-ly Mc-Gee Mc-Gaw._____ There were three crows sat

292

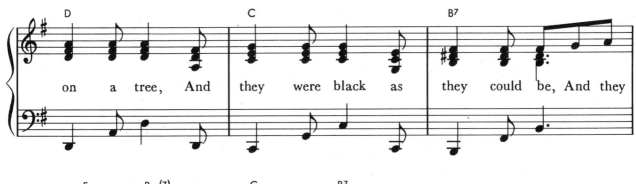

on a tree, And they were black as they could be, And they

all flapped their wings and cried, "Caw, caw, caw."

a tempo

Bil - ly Mc - Gee Mc - Gaw. And they Gaw.

2. Said one old crow unto his mate,
   Billy McGee McGaw.
   Said one old crow unto his mate,
   Oh, Billy McGee McGaw.
   Said one old crow unto his mate,
   "What shall we do for grub to ate?"
   And they all flapp'd their wings, *etc.*

3. "There lies a horse on yonder plain,"
   Billy McGee McGaw.
   "There lies a horse on yonder plain,"
   Oh, Billy McGee McGaw.
   "There lies a horse on yonder plain,
   Who's by some cruel butcher slain."
   And they all flapp'd their wings, *etc.*

4. "We'll perch ourselves on his backbone,"
   Billy McGee McGaw.
   "We'll perch ourselves on his backbone."
   Oh, Billy McGee McGaw.
   "We'll perch ourselves on his backbone,
   And eat his eyeballs one by one."
   And they all flapp'd their wings, *etc.*

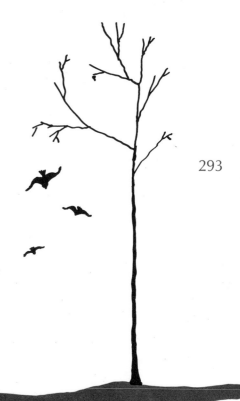

293

JOHNNY I HARDLY KNEW YE

This tune is most likely the direct antecedent of "When Johnny Comes Marching Home," although a Civil War bandmaster, Patrick Gilmore, claimed authorship.

STRUM: I-C

IRELAND

Moderately, in steady rhythm (♩.=88)

Arr. by N. L.

294

Verse:
While go-in' the road to sweet Ath-aye, hu-roo!— hu-roo!— While go-in' the road to sweet Ath-aye, hu-roo!— hu-roo! While— go-in' the road— to sweet Ath-aye, a stick in me hand and a drop in me eye,— A dole-ful dam-sel I heard cry: John-ny I hard-ly knew ye.

Refrain

With their drums and guns and guns and drums, hu-roo! — hu-roo! — With their drums and guns and guns and drums, hu-roo! — hu-roo! — With their drums and guns — and guns and drums, the en-e-my near-ly slew ye Oh — John-ny, my dear, you look so queer, John-ny I hard-ly knew ye.

2. Where are your eyes that looked so mild? Huroo! Huroo!
Where are your eyes that looked so mild? Huroo! Huroo!
Where are your eyes that looked so mild,
When my poor heart you first beguiled?
Ah! Why did you run from me and the child?
O, Johnny, I hardly knew ye!
Refrain

3. Where are the legs with which you run? Huroo! Huroo!
Where are the legs with which you run? Huroo! Huroo!
Where are the legs with which you run,
When first you went to carry a gun?
Indeed, your dancin' days are done!
O, Johnny, I hardly knew ye!
Refrain

4. It grieved my heart to see you sail. Huroo! Huroo!
It grieved my heart to see you sail. Huroo! Huroo!
It grieved my heart to see you sail,
Though from my heart you took leg-bail;
Like a cod, you're doubled up, head and tail.
O, Johnny, I hardly knew ye!
Refrain

5. I'm happy for to see you home. Huroo! Huroo!
I'm happy for to see you home. Huroo! Huroo!
I'm happy for to see you home,
All from the Island of Sulloon*
So low in the flesh, so high in bone.
O, Johnny, I hardly knew ye!
Refrain
* Ceylon

295

MEADOWS GREEN

A tale of great bravery to a typically heroic Slavic tune.

SLOVAKIA

Eng. Version by W. S.
Arr. by N. L.

STRUM: IX

Freely (♩ = 63)

Yan - ko grazed his cat - tle on mea - dows green.
Pá - sol Jan - ko dva vo - ly u há - ja.

Yan - ko grazed his cat - tle on mea - dows green. Yan - ko grazed his cat - tle where
Pá - sol Jan - ko dva vo - ly u há - ja. Pá - sol Jan - ko dva vo - ly

grass was lush and flow - ers fair. Grass was lush and flow - ers fair. Mea - dows green.
na ze - le - nom ú - ho - rí. Na ze - le - nom ú - ho - rí. Ú há - ja

296

♩ ♩ ♩ ♩ ♩ ♩ ♩ ♩

2. For — est rang — ers pass- ing through Mead- ows green. . . . .
For — est rang- ers, there were two. Mead- ows green. . . . .
"Give us trib- ute," they did say, "Or we'll send you on your way,
Or we'll send you on your way." Mead- ows green. . . . .

3. Yan — ko gaz — es on the fair Mead- ows green. . . . .
Turns to the con- niv- ing pair. Mead- ows green. . . . .
"You've no right to make de- mands. I'll not pay for com- mon lands.
I'll not pay for com- mon lands." Mead- ows green. . . . .

4. Yan — ko's ly- ing dead up- on Mead- ows green. . . . .
Rang — ers and the cat- tle gone. Mead- ows green. . . . .
There he lies so brave, so true, mid the rose- mary and the rue.
Mid the rose- mary and the rue. Mead- ows green. . . . .

2. Daj nám, Janko, halenu, u hája. (repeat)
Daj nám Janko halenu,
Spásol si nám d'atel'u, u hája.

3. Ja vám halenu nedám, u hája. (repeat)
Ja vám halenu nedám,
Ja sa s vami pojednám, u hája.

4. Tak sa oni jednali, u hája. (repeat)
Tak sa oni jednali,
Až Janíka zabili, u hája.

5. Leži Janík zabitý, u hája. (repeat)
Leži Janík zabitý,
Rozmajrínkom prikrytý, u hája.

6. Ktože ho tam narieka, u hája. (repeat)
Ktože ho tam narieka,
Otec, mati, frajerka, u hája.

IF YOU WANT TO WRITE TO ME

This is a rousing but moving song of the Spanish Civil War. The tune is of nineteenth century folk origin.

STRUM: IA

SPAIN

Eng. Version by W. S.
Arr. by N. L.

Moderately (♩ = 112)

If you want to write to me,
Si me quie-res es-cri-bir,

This is where to send a let-ter.
Ya sa-bes me pa-ra-der-o.

If you want to write to me,
Si me quie-res es-cri-bir,

This is
_Ya sa-_

298

2. O, the landlord of this inn
   Is a Moor who's named Mohammed. } twice
   And his customers all know
   His food is always hot and spicy. } twice

3. O, the appetizers are
   Rounds of bullets from machine-guns, } twice
   Followed quickly by some hand-grenades } twice
   And served with bursts of shrapnel.

299

2. Si tu quieres comer bien
   Barato y de buena forma } twice
   En el frente de Gandesa
   Alli tienen una fonda. } twice

3. En la entrada
   Hay un moro Mojama } twice
   Que te dice, "Pasa, pasa } twice
   Que quieres para comer."

4. El primer plato que dan
   Son granadas rompedoras } twice
   El segundo de metralla
   Para recordar memorias. } twice

PEAT BOG SOLDIERS

A song of the concentration camps during World War II. Grim, and deeply stirring.

STRUM: IX-A

GERMANY

Arr. by N. L.

Moderately slow (♩ = 92)

Far and wide as the eye can wan - der,
Wo - hin auch das Au - ge bli - cket,

Heath and bog are ev - ry - where.
Moor und Hel - de rings - he - rum.

Not a bird sings out to cheer us,
Vo - gel - sang uns nicht er - qui - cket,

300

Oaks are / stand - ing / gaunt and / bare.
Eich - en / steh - en / kahl und / krum.

Refrain

We are the / peat - bog / sol - - diers; / We're
Wir sind die / Moor - sol - da - - ten; / Und

march - ing / with our / spades / To the
zieh - er / mit dem / Spa - - / ten Ins

1. bog. ___
Moor. ___

2. bog. ___
Moor. ___

301

2. Up and down, the guards are pacing.
   No one, no one can go through.
   Flight would mean a sure death facing.
   Guns and barb'd wire greet our view.
   We are the peat-bog soldiers;
   We're marching with our spades } *twice*
   To the bog.

3. But, for us there is no complaining.
   Winter will in time be past;
   One day we shall cry, rejoicing,
   "Homeland, dear, you're mine at last!"
   Then will the peat-bog soldiers
   March no more with their spades } *twice*
   To the bog.

2. Auf und nieder gehen die Posten,
   Keiner, keiner kann hindurch.
   Flucht wird nur das Leben kosten,
   Vielfach ist umzäunt die Burg.
   Wir sind die Moorsoldaten;
   Und siehen mit dem Spaten } *twice*
   Ins Moor.

3. Doch für uns gibt es kein Klagen,
   Ewig kann's nicht Winter sein.
   Einmal werden froh wir sagen,
   "Heimat, du bist wieder mein!"
   Dann ziehen die Moorsoldaten
   *Nicht mehr mit dem Spaten } *twice*
   Ins Moor.

* **Nicht** *should come on the down beat.*

THE BALLAD OF THE BOLL WEEVIL

There is a perverse sympathy for the boll weevil who survives all attempts to eradicate him.
Many Negroes identify with him in
"lookin' for a home."

STRUM: IIIA

UNITED STATES

Arr. by N. L.

Lively (♩=84)

Verse

The boll wee-vil is a lit-tle black bug, come from Mex-i-co they say; Come all the way to Tex-as, just a look-in' for a place to stay, just a-look-in' for a home, just a-look-in' for a home.

302

2. The first time I saw the boll weevil,
   He was settin' on the square.
   The next time I saw the boll weevil,
   He had all his fam'ly there. He was lookin' for a home.
   He was lookin' for a home. He was lookin', *etc.*
   Refrain:

3. The farmer took the boll weevil.
   And he put him in the hot old sand.
   The weevil said, "This is mighty hot,
   But I'll stand it like a man. This'll be my home.
   This'll be my home. This'll be my," *etc.*
   Refrain:

4. The farmer took the boll weevil,
   And he put him in a lump of ice.
   The weevil said to the farmer,
   "This is mighty cool and nice. This'll be my home.
   This'll be my home. This'll be my," *etc.*
   Refrain:

5. The boll weevil said to the farmer;
   "You can ride in your Ford machine,
   But when I get thru with your cotton,
   Can't buy no gasoline. Won't have no home.
   Won't have no home. Won't have no," *etc.*

6. The merchant got half of the cotton.
   The boll weevil got the rest.
   Didn't leave the farmer's wife
   But one old cotton dress, and it's full of holes.
   It's full of holes. It's full of, *etc.*
   Refrain:

7. The farmer said to the merchant,
   "We're in an awful fix.
   The boll weevil ate all the cotton up,
   And left us only sticks. We're goin' on home.
   We're goin' on home. We're goin' on", *etc.*
   Refrain:

8. The farmer said to the merchant,
   "I want some meat and meal."
   "Get away from here, you son of a gun,
   You've got boll weevils in your fiel'. Gonna get your home.
   Gonna get your home. Gonna get your", *etc.*
   Refrain:

9. The farmer said to the merchant,
   "We ain't made but only one bale,
   And before we'll give you that one,
   We'll fight and go to jail. We'll have a home.
   We'll have a home. We'll have a", *etc.*
   Refrain:

303

NO MORE AUCTION BLOCK FOR ME

A stirring and vital song of protest, as meaningful today as during the Civil War.

STRUM: IA or IXA

UNITED STATES

Arr. by N. L.

Slowly ($\quarternote = 72$)

(Chorus) No more auc-tion block for me, no more, no more.

304

No more auc-tion block for me, man-y thous-and gone,

2. No more driver's lash for me, *etc.*

3. No more peck of corn for me, *etc.*

4. No more pint of salt for me, *etc.*

5. No more mistress call for me, *etc.*
Repeat first verse.

MAGIC, MYSTERIES, MERMAIDS AND SUCH

THE LEPRECHAUN

It's hard to catch a leprechaun and still harder to hold him. For the uninitiated, cruiskeen is a small jar and mountain-dew is pottheen (illicit whiskey).

2. With   tip-toe step and beating heart,
Quite   softly I drew nigh.
'Twas   mischief in his merry face,
A   twinkle in his eye.
He   hammered and sang with tiny voice,
And   drank his mountain dew,
And I   laughed to think he was caught at last,
But the   fairy was laughing too!

3. As   quick as thought I seized the elf.
"Your   fairy purse!" I cried.
"The   purse," he said, " 'Tis in her hand,
The   lady by your side".
I   turned to look; the elf was off!
Then   what was I to do?
O, I   laughed to think what a fool I'd been,
And the   fairy was laughing too!

THE FAIRY'S LOVE SONG

This bears a strong resemblance to the Scottish tune "Ca' the Yowes." An elegant, mystical love ballad.

STRUM: II A ($\dot{\ } = 60$)

SCOTLAND

Arr. by N. L.

Refrain

Why should I sit and sigh,
Tha mi sgith 's mi leam fhin
Pull - ing brack-en, pull - ing brack-en?
bua-in a rain-ich, bua-in a rain-ich

Why should I sit and sigh
Tha mi sgith 's mi leam fhin
On the hill - side drear - y?
bua-ain a rain - ich da-onn-an.

Verse

When I see the plov - er ris - ing
Sul an tom - ain braigh-an tom - ain
Or the cur - lew wheel - ing,
cul an tom - ain bhoidh - ich,

Then I trow my mor - tal lov - er
Cul an tom - ain braigh-an tom - ain
Back to me is steal - ing.
huil - e lath - a m'on - ar.

308

2. Ah! But there is something wanting.
   Oh! But I am weary.
   Come, my blithe and bonnie lad,
   Come over the knoll to cheer me.

2. Cul an tomain braigh an tomain,
   Cul an tomain bhoidhich.
   Cul an tomain braigh an tomain,
   Huile latha m'onar.

This song and the two
following reveal
remnants of folk belief
in sorcery, wizardry
and the magic ability
to change form in
the pursuit of love.

THE TWO MAGICIANS

STRUM: Ic

ENGLAND

Lively (♩.= 108)

Arr. by N. L.

Verse

1. Oh, she looked out of the win-dow, as white as an-y milk, But

he looked in-to the win-dow, as black as an-y silk.

Refrain

310

"Hul-loa, hul-loa, hul-loa, hul-loa, You coal black smith. You have

done me no harm.___ You nev-er shall change my maid-en name that

I have kept so long. I'd ra-ther die a maid and be

bu-ried all in my grave, Than to have such a nas-ty, hus-ky, dus-ky,

mus-ky, fus-ky, coal-black smith. A maid-en I'll re main".

Fine

Verse

2. Then she be-came a duck, a duck all on a stream, And
3. Then she be-came a hare, a hare up on the plain, And
4. Then she be-came a fly, a fly all in the air, And

he be-came a wa-ter dog and fetched her back a-gain.
he be-came a grey-hound dog and fetched her back a-gain.
he be-came a spi - - der and fetched her to his lair.

D.S.al Fine

311

METAMORPHOSIS

The story is the same; the tune is lively and lilting. In this version, instead of waiting to be caught, she gives up in the face of his persistency.

FRANCE

STRUM: Ic

Eng. version by W. S.
Arr. by N. L.

Moderately fast (♩.= 100)

(He) As I went out one morn - ing, morn - ing so
J'ai fait u - ne maî - tres - se, y-a pas long -

fair, _____ I met a love - ly maid - en
temps, _____ J'ai fait u - ne maî - tres - se,

with flax - en hair. _____ I'm going to see her
y-a pas long - temps. _____ J'i - raî la voir di -

Sun - day, my love to de - clare, _____ And
man - che sans plus tar - der, _____ Je

win un - num - bered kiss - es from lips so rare. _____
pren - drai sur sa bou - che un doux bai - ser. _____

312

2. *She* Young man, before you kiss me, try as you will, (*repeat*)
   I shall become a wild doe and run up the hill,
   Because I do not like you and never will.

3. *He* If you become a doe and flee 'cross the plain, (*repeat*)
   Then I'll become a hunter, and fetch you back again,
   For parted from your sweetness I'll not remain.

4. *She* If you become a hunter, I'll rove about. (*repeat*)
   I'll jump into the river and then be a trout,
   And down among the rocks I'll swim in and out.

5. *He* If you become a trout, an angler I'll be. (*repeat*)
   I'll cast my line and catch you where stream meets the sea,
   For no one else shall have you, no one but me.

6. *She* If you become an angler, casting my way, (*repeat*)
   Then I'll become a rose and in my garden stay,
   Because my answer to you shall e'er be nay.

7. *He* If you become a rosebud, glist'ning with dew, (*repeat*)
   Then I'll become a gard'ner and when I find you,
   I'll let no one come near, 'til to me you're true.

8. *She* If you become a gard'ner, I'm not undone. (*repeat*)
   I'll climb right o'er the convent wall and then be a nun,
   For I will grant no favors to you, not one.

9. *He* If you become a nun, behind cloistered walls, (*repeat*)
   Then I'll become the doctor who on the cloister calls,
   For I shall never lose you, what e'er befalls.

10. *She* If you become the doctor, then I shall die. (*repeat*)
    I'll ask the Lord to take me to my home on high,
    And then to you at last I'll have said, "Goodbye."

11. *He* If you go up to heaven, I'll race you there. (*repeat*)
    I shall become St. Peter, your home to prepare,
    And, for eternity, we, the bliss, will share.

12. *She* Oh, if you are St. Peter, with golden key, (*repeat*)
    Then I'll come down to earth again and say, "Marry me."
    For I have never seen such persistency.

313

O, SALLY MY DEAR

A variant of the text and a beautiful modal tune.

STRUM: Vв

ENGLAND

Arr. by N. L.

Moderately—with a lilt (♩=108)

Oh,— Sal-ly, my dear, but I wish I could woo you. Oh,— Sal-ly, my dear, but I wish I could woo you. She laughed and re-plied, "And would woo-ing un-do you?" Sing fal the did-dle-i do, sing whack fal the did-dle day.

314

2. O, Sally my dear, but your cheek I could kiss it.   (*repeat*)
   She laugh'd and replied, "If you did, would you miss it?"
   Sing fal, etc.

3. O, Sally my dear, I would love you and wed you.   (*repeat*)
   She laughed and replied, "Then don't say I misled you."
   Sing fal, etc.

4. If lassies were blackbirds and lassies were thrushes,   (*repeat*)
   How soon the young men would go beating the bushes.
   Sing fal, etc.

5. If the women were hares and raced 'round the mountain,   (*repeat*)
   How soon the young men would be busy a–hunting.
   Sing fal, etc.

6. If the women were ducks and swum 'round the water,   (*repeat*)
   The men would turn drakes and be soon swimming after.
   Sing fal, etc.

THE GREAT SILKIE

Silkies are supernatural seal-folk living in the sea, who occasionally come ashore, posing as ordinary men. Many Scottish island families claim seal men asancestors.

STRUM: VB or IIB

SCOTLAND

Arr. by N. L.

Moderately (♩=110)

An earth - ly nour - ris sits and sings, And aye ____ she sings, ____ "Ba, li - ly wean! ____ Lit - tle ken I ____ my bairn - is fa - ther, Far less the land that he stops in".

(♪)   ♩ ♩ ♩   ♩   ♩   ♩   ♩ ♩ ♩   ♩   ♩ (♪)

2. Then   one   a — rose   at   her   bed — foot, ...
   And a   grumb — ly guest,   I'm   sure, was   he; ....
            "Here   am   I,   thy   bairn — is   fath — er,
   Al —   though I   be   not   com — e —   lie." ......

3. "I   am   a   man   up — on   the   land, ...
   And   I'm   a   sil —   kie   in   the   sea; ....
   And   when   I'm   far   and   far   frae   land ......
   My   dwell — ing is   in   Sule Sker — rie." ......

4. "It   was   na   weel," quoth the   maid — en   fair, ...
   "It   was   na   weel,   in — deed," quoth she, ...
            "That the Great Sil — kie o   Sule Sker — rie
   Should hae come   and   aught   a   bairn to   me." ......

5. Now   he   has   ta'en   a   purse of   gold, ...
   And   he   has   put it up — on   her   knee, ...
   Say-in', "Gi'e to   me   my   lit — tle young son, ...
   And   take   thee up   thy   nour — ris fee." ......

6. "It shall come   to   pass on a   sum — mer's day, ...
   When the sun   shines hot   on   ev' — ry   stone, ...
   That   I   will take   my   lit — tle young son, ...
   And   teach him   for   to   swim   the   foam." ....

7. "And   thou   shall mar — ry . a proud, fine gun — ner,
   A   proud, fine gun — ner I'm sure   he'll be; ......
   And the   ver — y first shot   that e'er   he   shoots, ...
   He'll   shoot both my   young son   and   me." ......

THE DEVIL AND THE FARMER'S WIFE

The story of a farmer who tries to get rid of his shrewish wife with the aid of Old Nick. There are many variants of the text and tune.

STRUM: IA

UNITED STATES

Arr. by N. L.

Lively (♩=176)

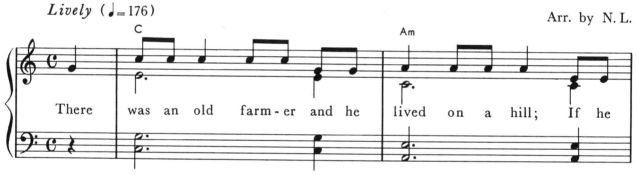

There was an old farm-er and he lived on a hill; If he

Refrain

ain't moved a-way, he's a-liv-in' there still. Sing hi did-dle I

did-dle I fye, Did-dle I did-dle I day.

2. The   Devil he came to the farmer one day,—
   Says,   "One of your family I'm takin' away."
   Refrain

3. "O,   please don't take my eldest son,
   There's   work on the farm that's got to be done."
   Refrain

4.   "Take my wife with the joy of my heart,
   And I   hope by golly that you never part."
   Refrain

5. The   Devil put the old woman into a sack,
   And   down the road went clickity clack.
   Refrain

6. And   when they got to the fork of the road,
   He   says, "Old woman, you're a hell of a load."
   Refrain

7. And   when they got to the gates of Hell,
   He said, "Stoke up the fire, boys, we'll roast her well."
   Refrain

8. Then   up stepp'd a devil with ball and chain;
   She   upped with her foot and kicked out his brain.
   Refrain

9. Then   nine little devils went running up the wall,
   Crying, "Take her back, Daddy, she'll murder us all."
   Refrain

10. Well, the old man was peekin' thru a crack,
   When he seen the old Devil come a-bringin' her back.
   Refrain

11.   "Here's your wife both sound and well,
   If she'd stayed any longer she'd a-torn up Hell."
   Refrain

12. "I've   been a devil most all of my life,
   But I   never knew what Hell was 'till I met with your wife."
   Refrain

13. This   proves that the women are better than the men,
   They can all go to Hell and come back again.
   Refrain

THE WREN BOYS

From County Cork, this is related to the wassailing songs. It has an unusual tune and harmonic structure. Scholars think the custom of parading a dead wren around the countryside is anti-aristocratic in origin.

STRUM: I-c

IRELAND (County Cork)

Arr. by N. L.

Lively (♩.=104)

The wran, the wran, the king of all birds on St. Ste-phen's day was caught in the furze, Al-though he is lit-tle his fam-i-ly's great, Put your hand in your pock-et and give us a trate; Sing hol-ly, sing i-vy, sing i-vy, sing hol-ly, A drop just to drink it would drown mel-an-chol-y, And if you draw it of the best, We hope in heav-en your soul will rest, but if you draw it of the small, It won't a-gree with the wran boys at all.

FOLK HYMNS
AND SPIRITUALS

321

THE CHRIST CHILD'S LULLABY

A most beautiful modal tune, it has the "drone" common to so many songs of the Hebrides.

STRUM: VB

SCOTLAND

Arr. by N. L.

Moderately (♩=120)

My joy, my love, my dar - ling Thou! My

322

trea - sure new, my rap - ture Thou. My

come - ly beau - teous babe - son Thou, Un -

worthy — y I to tend to Thee.

Hal — le — lu — i — a,

Hal — le — lu — i — a,

Hal — le — lu — i — a,

Hal — le — lu — i — a.

2. White sun and hope of light art Thou! . . . .
   Of love the heart and eye art Thou! . . . .
   Tho' but a ten — der babe, I bow . . . . . .
   In heav'n — ly rap — ture un — to Thee. . . . .
   Refrain:

323

AMEN

A wonderfully simple Christmas spiritual for solo and group answers.

UNITED STATES

Arr. by N. L.

STRUM: IIA

Moderately (♩ = 110)

324

THE VIRGIN MARY HAD-A ONE SON

Much the same kind of uncomplicated reverence as "Amen." Both are from the singing of Peggy Seeger.

STRUM: I-A

UNITED STATES

Arr. by N. L.

Slowly, but rhythmically (♩=76)

(Chorus) The ___ Vir - gin ___ Ma - ry had - a one ___ son,

Mm - mmm, ___ Glo - ry hal - le - lu - jah. Mm - mmm, ___

Glo - ry hal - le - lu - jah, Glo - ry be to the

(Alternate ending)

new - born King. ___ new - born King.

325

2. Mary, what you gonna call that purty little baby?
   Mm Mm Glory halleluja.
3. Some call him a one thing, think I'll call him counc'lor.
   Mm Mm Glory halleluja.
4. Some call him a one thing, think I'll call him 'Manuel.
   Mm Mm Glory halleluja.
5. Some call him a one thing, think I'll call him Jesus.
   Mm Mm Glory halleluja.
   Repeat first verse.

STRANGER

A nineteenth century text set to an eighteenth century tune; it's a moving personal statement of mixed fear and hope.

Strum: VB or IIB

United States

Arr. by N. L.

Moderately slow ($\sharp = 60$)

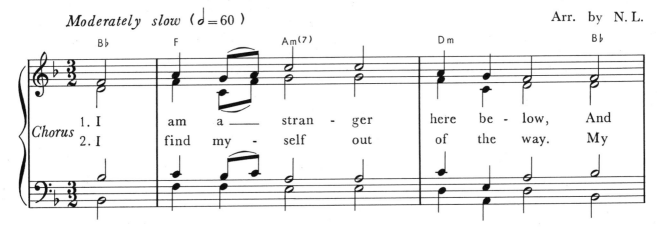

Chorus
1. I am a stran-ger here be-low, And
2. I find my-self out of the way. My

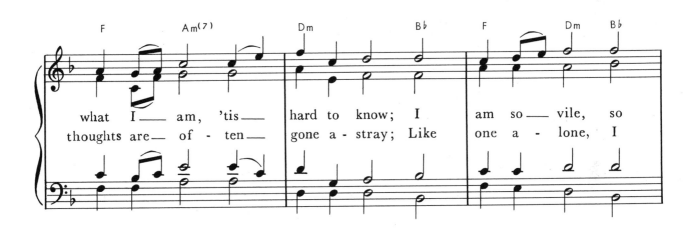

what I am, 'tis hard to know; I am so vile, so
thoughts are of-ten gone a-stray; Like one a-lone, I

prone to sin, I fear that I'm not born a-gain.
seem to be. Oh, is there a-ny one like me?

327

3. 'Tis seldom I can ever see
   Myself as I would wish to be;
   What I desire, I can't attain
   And what I hate, I can't refrain.

4. My nature is so giv'n to sin,
   Which makes my duty so unclean,
   That when I count up all the cost,
   If not free grace, then I am lost.

ALL MY TRIALS

A spiritual from the Bahamas, it is different melodically and harmonically from most of the spirituals from the South.

STRUM: IX

BAHAMAS

Arr. by N. L.

Moderately, with very free rhythm (♩ = 60)

Verse

D   Am⁽⁷⁾

If re - li-gion was a thing that mon-ey could buy, _____ The

328

D   *ten*   F#m   G   Gm

rich would live and the poor would die. _____

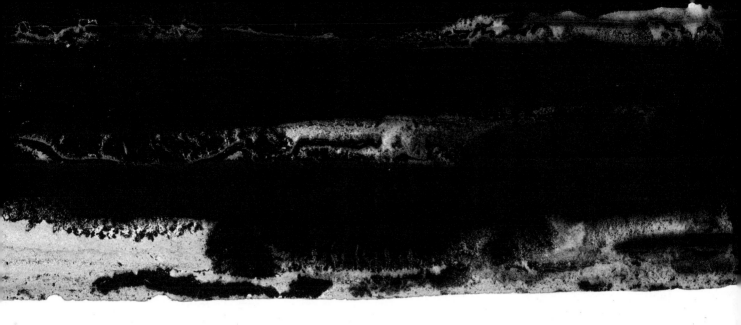

2. Now, hush little baby, don't you cry,
   You know that man is born to die.
   Refrain

3. I had a little book, 'twas given to me,
   And ev'ry leaf spelled victory.
   Refrain

OLD TIME RELIGION

One of the best-known gospel hymns, it stems from a Negro spiritual.

STRUM: Ia

UNITED STATES

Refrain Spirited ($\quad$ = 76)

Arr. by N. L.

330

(same tune as refrain)

Verse 1. It was good enough for father, *(three times)*
It's good enough for me.
Refrain

Verse 2. It was good for Paul and Silas, *(three times)*
It's good enough for me.
Refrain

Verse 3. It was good for the Hebrew children, *(three times)*
It's good enough for me.
Refrain

Refrain Give me that old time re-li-gion, Give me that old time re-li-gion, Give me that old time re-li-gion,——— It's good e-nough for me.

WHEN JESUS WEPT

This is a composed Round, from "The New England Psalm Singer," published in 1770.

UNITED STATES

William Billings

Moderately (♩ = 96)

1 When Je - sus wept, _____ the fall - ing tear

2 in mer - cy flowed _____ be - yond all bound.

3 When Je - sus groaned, a trem - b'ling fear

4 seized all _____ the guil - ty world _____ a - round.

331

WONDROUS LOVE

This is considered a "down-east spiritual" related to another spiritual, "Villulia."
It is an inspired wedding of text and tune.

STRUM: IX

UNITED STATES

Moderately slow, but with movement (♩ = 84)

Arr. by N. L.

(Chorus) What won-drous love is this, O, my soul! O, my

soul! What won-drous love is this, O, my

soul! What won-drous love is this, that

caus'd the Lord— of bliss To send such per-fect peace to my soul, to my soul, To send such per-fect peace to my soul?

2. Ye wingéd seraphs fly, bear the news, bear the news!
   Ye wingéd seraphs fly, bear the news!
   Ye wingéd seraphs fly, like comets through the sky,
   With loud and joyful cry, bear the news, bear the news!
   With loud and joyful cry, bear the news!

3. To God and to the Lamb, I will sing, I will sing.
   To God and to the Lamb, I will sing.
   To God and to the Lamb, Jehovah, great I AM,
   And Christ the Son of Man, I will sing, I will sing,
   And Christ the Son of Man, I will sing.

4. When we're from sorrow free, we'll sing on, we'll sing on.
   When we're from sorrow free, we'll sing on.
   When we're from sorrow free, we'll rise and joyful be,
   And through eternity, we'll sing on, we'll sing on,
   And through eternity, we'll sing on.

A COWBOY'S PRAYER

Simple and naïve, in that the imagery of the text is so related to everyday life. The tune is of Irish origin. A very moving prayer.

STRUM: IIIB or IIB

UNITED STATES

Moderately Slow (♩ = 80)

Arr. by N. L.

334

Oh Lord, please hear___ me, lend me Thine ear; The
You've blessed the round - up through___ the years. Now,
The prai - rie fires___ won't You please stop? Make

tale of a trou - bled___ cow - boy to hear. No
please don't for - get___ the grow___ ing steers.
thun - der___ roll,___ make the rain___ to drop. Our

doubt___ the pray'r___ may seem to be strange,___ But I
Wa - ter the lands___ with brooks and with rills ___ For the
moun - tains are peaceful,___ our prai - ries se - rene.___ Oh___

ask you to bless our cat - tle range.
cat - tle that roam on a thou - sand hills.
Lord, for the cat - tle, please keep___ them green.

HOP UP, JUMP UP

A Shaker hymn which was accompanied by motions and gestures. "Shaker ritualism was a true folk art."

STRUM: II A

UNITED STATES

Arr. by N. L.

Lively (𝅗𝅥 = 84)

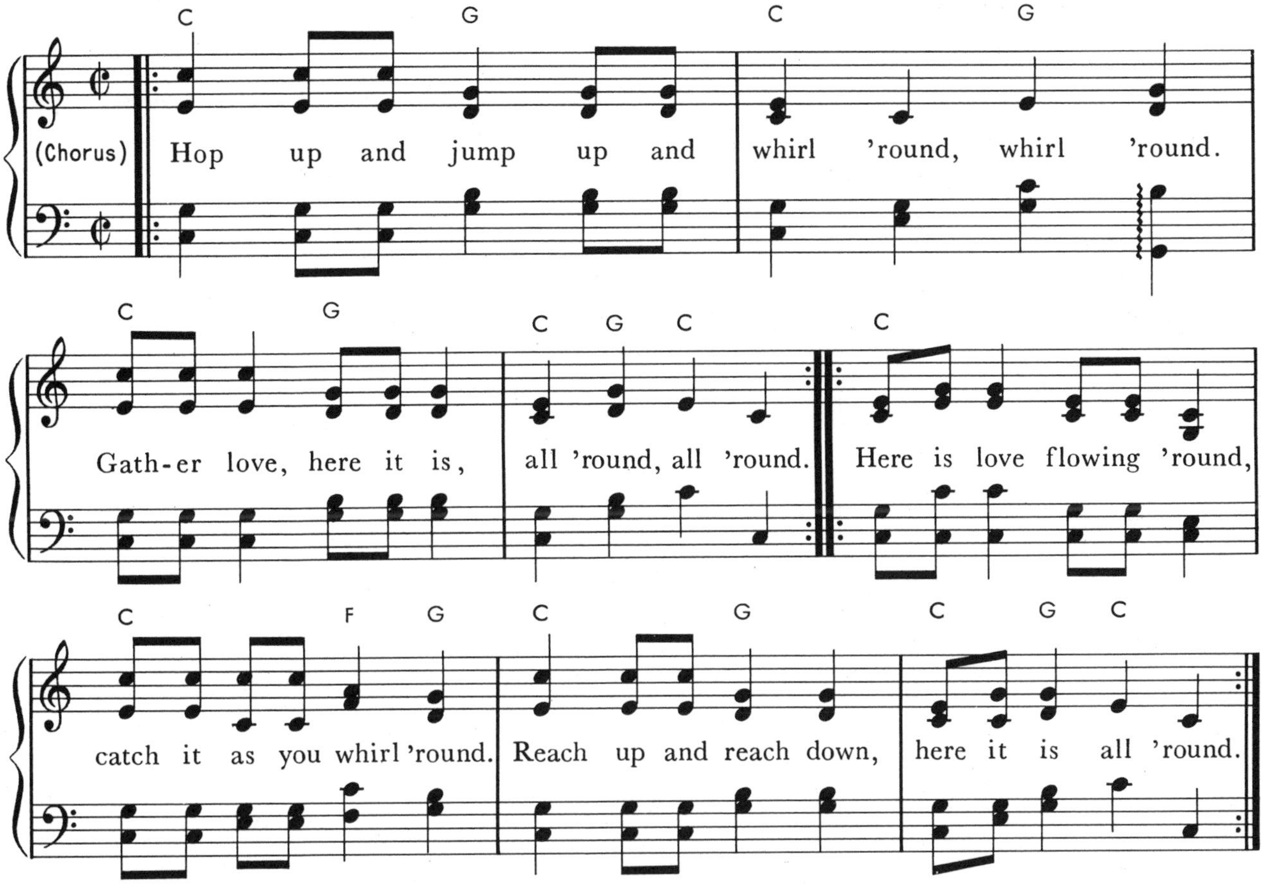

C G C G
(Chorus)
Hop up and jump up and whirl 'round, whirl 'round.
C G C G C C
Gath-er love, here it is, all 'round, all 'round. Here is love flowing 'round,
C F G C G C G C
catch it as you whirl 'round. Reach up and reach down, here it is all 'round.

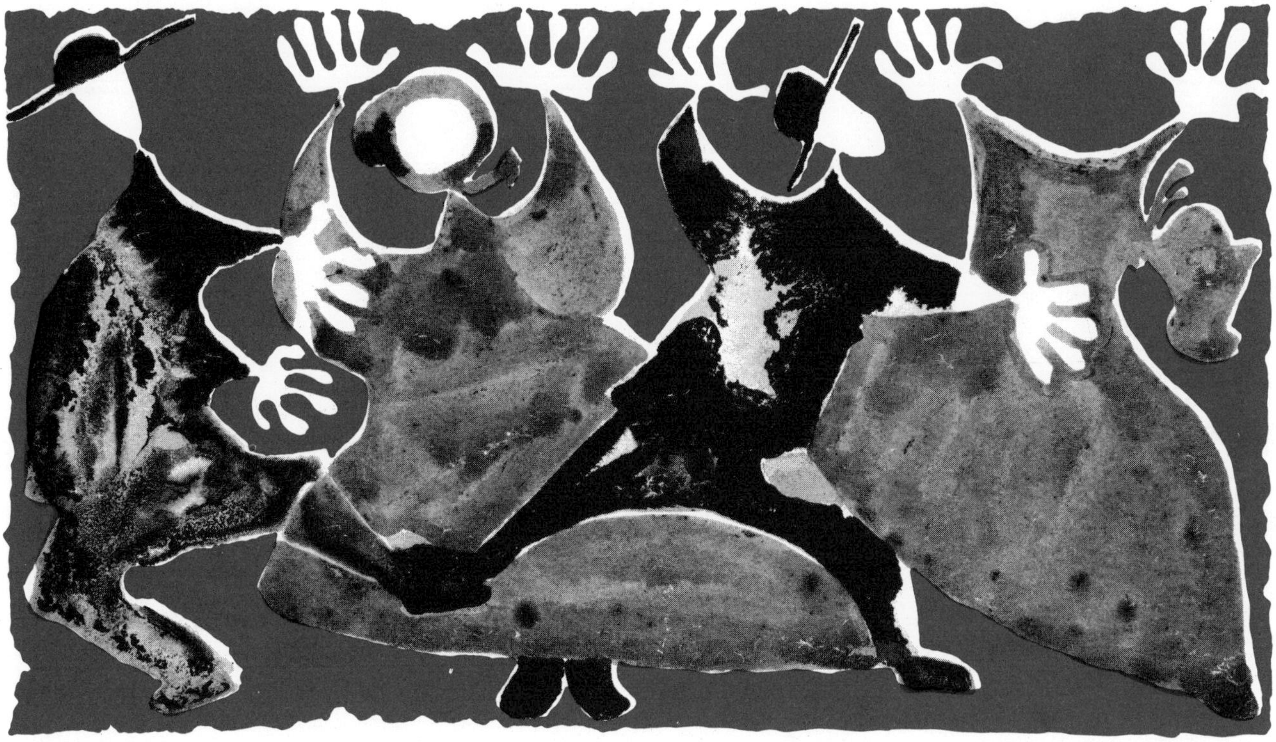

SIMPLE GIFTS

This is another Shaker hymn of the "Mother Ann's Work" period.
(Ann Lee, 1736-1784, leader of the Shakers.)

STRUM: Ia

UNITED STATES

Arr. by N. L.

Moderately (♩ = 92)

(Chorus) 'Tis the gift to be sim-ple, 'tis the gift to be free, 'Tis the gift to come down where we ought to be, And when we find our selves ___ in the place just ___ right 'Twill ___ be in the val-ley of love and de-light.

When true sim-pli-ci-ty is gained, To bow and to bend we will

336

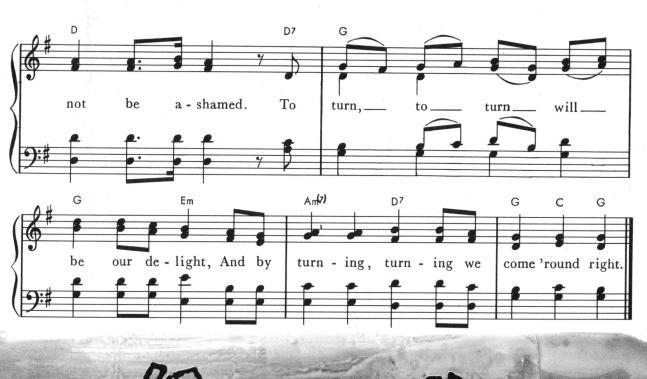

not be a-shamed. To turn, ___ to ___ turn ___ will ___

be our de-light, And by turn-ing, turn-ing we come 'round right.

LOOBY LOO

Usually considered a children's singing game, this was performed in 1857 "with appropriate gestures" by two Shaker "sisters" from the Canterbury Community.

338

STRUM: I-C

UNITED STATES

Arr. by N. L.

Rhythmically - not too fast (♩.=120)

I put my right hand in, I put my right hand out, I

give my hand a shake, shake, shake, and turn my-self a - bout.

Refrain

Here we go, loo - by loo, here we go, loo - by light.

Here we go, loo - by loo, all on a Sa - tur-day night.

Verses:

2. I put my left hand in, *etc.*
3. I put my right foot in, *etc.*
4. I put my left foot in, *etc.*
5. I put my right elbow in, *etc.*
6. I put my left elbow in, *etc.*
7. I put my whole self in, *etc.*

THIS LITTLE LIGHT OF MINE

A wonderful "swinging" gospel song.

STRUM: I-A

UNITED STATES

Arr. by N. L.

Moderately (♩ = 138)

Refrain

340

day,   ev-'ry   way,   Ev-'ry   day,   ev-'ry

way, ——   gon-na   let   my   lit-tle   light   shine. ——   *Fine*

Verse (Solo voice)

On   Mon-day   he   gave   me   the   gift ——   of   love, ——   on   Tues-day   peace   came

Hum. ——   Hum. ——

341

from a-bove, ——   on   Wednes-day   he   told   me   to   have ——   more   faith, ——   on

Hum. ——   Hum. ——

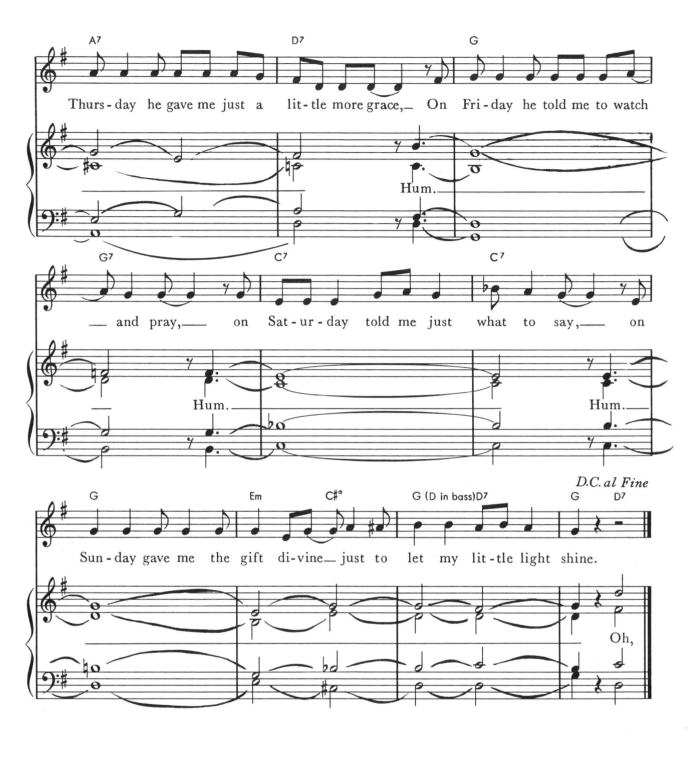

Thurs-day he gave me just a lit-tle more grace,— On Fri-day he told me to watch — and pray,— on Sat-ur-day told me just what to say,— on Sun-day gave me the gift di-vine— just to let my lit-tle light shine.

Hum. Hum. Hum.

D.C. al Fine

Oh,

KUM BA YA

STRUM: VB or IB

Slowly (♩ = 68)

NIGERIA

Arr. by N. L.

(Chorus) Kum ba ya, my Lord, Kum ba ya. Kum ba ya, my Lord, Kum ba ya. Kum ba ya, my Lord, Kum ba ya. Oh, Lord, _____ Kum ba ya.

1. Someone's singing, Lord, Kum ba ya. (*three times*)
   Oh, Lord, Kum ba ya.
   Refrain

2. Someone's crying, Lord, Kum ba ya. (*three times*)
   Oh, Lord, Kum ba ya.
   Refrain

3. Someone's praying, Lord, Kum ba ya. (*three times*)
   Oh, Lord, Kum ba ya.
   Refrain

TWELVE GATES TO THE CITY

This refers to "Revelations, Chapter 21, Verse 12."
A rousing jubilant spiritual.

STRUM: XI

UNITED STATES

Arr. by N. L.

Rhythmically - Not too fast ($\quarternote = 108$)

Refrain

Oh, what a beau-ti-ful cit-y, Oh, what a beau-ti-ful cit - y, Oh, what a beau-ti-ful cit-y, Twelve gates— to the cit-y, hal-le-lu- -jah.

Fine

Verse 1 only

1. Three gates— to the east, three gates— to the west, three gates— to the north,— three gates— to the south, There's

twelve gates— to the cit-y, hal-le lu- - jah. *D.C. al Fine*

Verses 2,3 & 4

2. Oh, who are those chil-dren dressed— in red?— There's
must be the chil-dren that Mo - ses led.— There's

twelve gates——— to the cit-y, hal - le -
twelve gates——— to the cit-y, hal - le -

lu - - - - jah. It
lu - - - - - jah.

D.C. al Fine

3. My God done just what He said
   There's twelve gates to the city, hallelujah.
   He healed the sick and he raised the dead.
   There's twelve gates, *etc.*
   Refrain:

4. When I get to Heav'n gonna sing and shout,
   There's twelve gates to the city, hallelujah.
   Ain't nobody there gonna put me out.
   There's twelve gates, *etc.*
   Refrain:

LITTLE MOSES

A wonderful example of the use of Bible stories in country and hillbilly music. Almost like a spiritual.

STRUM: I-B or V-B

UNITED STATES

Moderately fast ($\quarternote$ = 152)

Arr. by N. L.

(Chorus) A - way by the riv - er so clear, _____ the

la - dies were wend - ing their way, _____ And

Pha - raoh's young daugh - ter stepp'd down in the wa - ter to

346

bathe in the cool of the day. _____ Be -

fore it was dark, she o-pen'd the ark, and—

found the sweet in-fant was there. _____

(♩)

2. A — way   by the wa — ters so blue, ...
   The in — fant was lone — ly and sad. . . . .
   She took him in pit — y and thought him so pret — ty,
   And made   lit-tle Mo — ses so glad. . . . .
   She call'd him her own, her beau — ti — ful son, ...
   And sent for a nurse that was near. . . . .

3. A — way   by the ri — ver so clear, ...
   They car — ried the beau — ti — ful child, ...
   To his ten — der moth — er, his sis — ter and broth — er,
   And Mo — ses look'd hap — py and smiled. . . . .
   His moth — er so good did all that she could . . . . .
   To rear him and teach him with care. . . . .

4. A — way   by the sea that was red, ...
   Lit-tle Mo — ses the ser — vant of God, ...
   While in Him con — fid — ed, the sea was di — vid — ed,
   As up — ward he lift — ed his rod. . . . .
   The Jews safe — ly cross'd, while King Pha — raoh's host . . . . . .
   Was drown'd in the wa — ter and lost. . . . .

5. A — way   on a moun — tain so high, ...
   And the last one that e — ver — would see. . . . .
   While in Him vic — to — ri ous, his hope was most glo — rious,
   He'd soon o — ver Jor — dan be free. . . . .
   When his la — bor did cease, he de — par — ted in peace, ...
   And rest — ed in Heav — en a — bove. . . . .

347

HALLELUJAH

A baptismal shout.

STRUM: IA

Vigorously (𝅗𝅥 = 96)

UNITED STATES

Arr. by N. L.

348

THE LORD'S MY SHEPHERD

An archaic setting of the 23rd Psalm which is unusually poetic. The tune is eighteenth century Scottish.

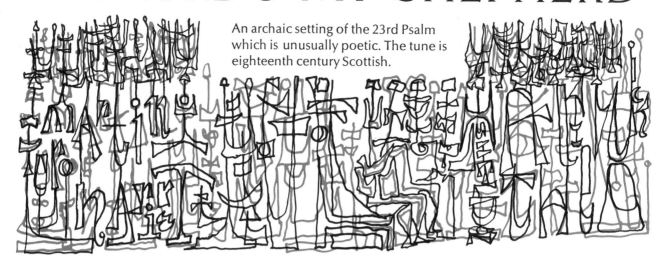

STRUM: VIB or IIB

SCOTLAND

Moderately slow (♩ = 96)

Arr. by N. L.

1. The Lord's my shep - herd, I'll not want; He makes me down to lie. In pas - tures green, He lead - eth me, The

2. My soul he doth re - store a - gain And me to walk to does make With - in the paths of right - eous - 'ness E'en

350

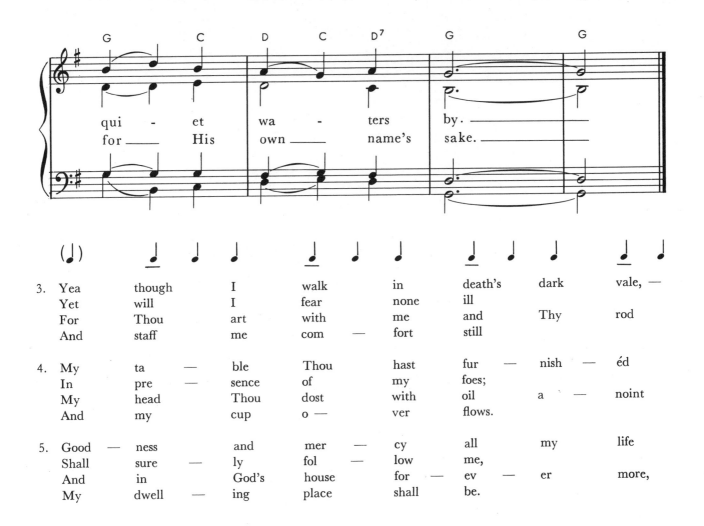

quiet waters by.
for His own name's sake.

(♩♩)

3. Yea though I walk in death's dark vale, —
Yet will I fear none ill
For Thou art with me and Thy rod
And staff me com — fort still

4. My ta — ble Thou hast fur — nish — éd
In pre — sence of my foes;
My head Thou dost with oil a — noint
And my cup o — ver flows.

5. Good — ness and mer — cy all my life
Shall sure — ly fol — low me,
And in God's house for — ev — er more,
My dwell — ing place shall be.

DONA NOBIS PACEM

This is a sixteenth century Round, generally attributed to Palestrina. The unconscious wish behind every prayer: "Grant us peace."

LATIN HYMN

Slowly, but with movement (♩ = 69)

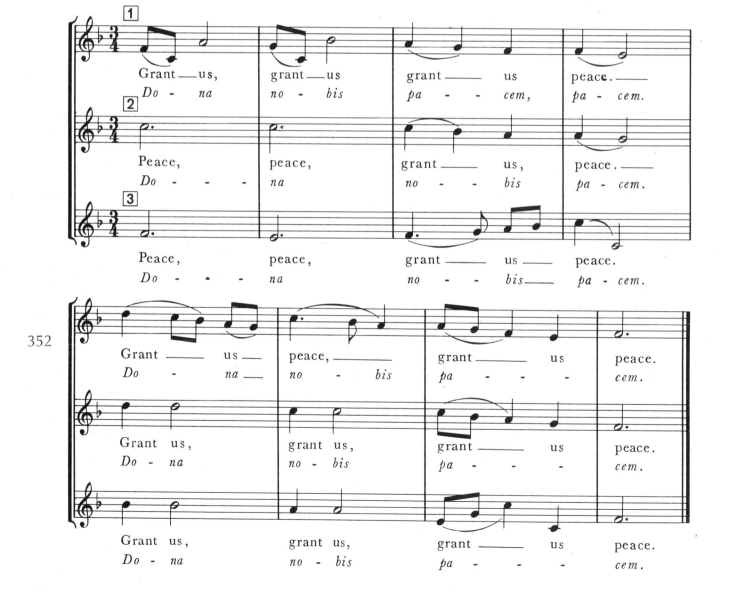

352

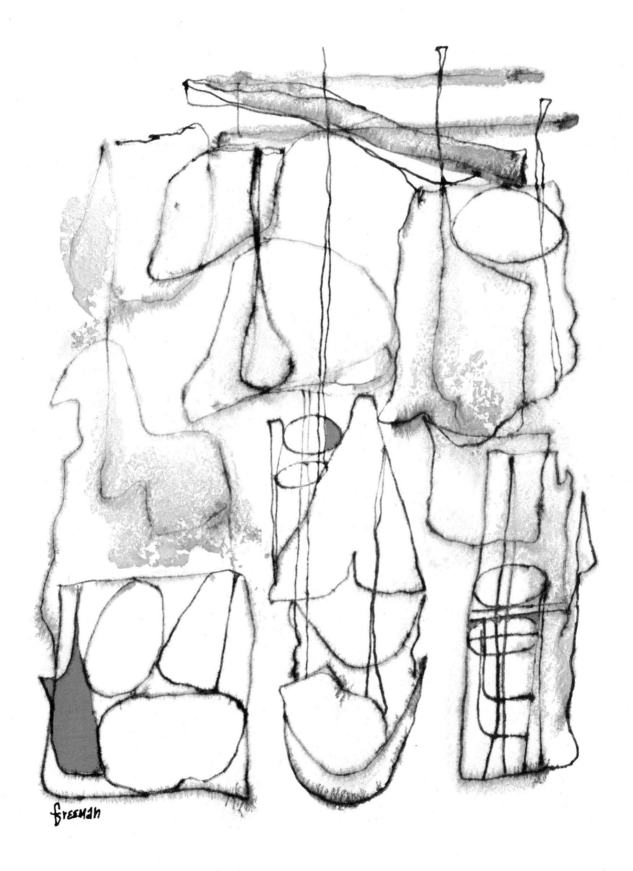

NOTES ON THE GUITAR

In our approach to the guitar, it is our purpose to suggest suitable accompaniments, rather than to offer a teaching method. All of the strums suggested should be playable by any guitarist of average ability. In instances where there is any question of difficulty, we have recommended more than one.

Strums basically break down into two categories: Thumb-pluck or Thumbstrum. There are, of course, an infinite number of variations of each of these, plus combinations of the two. We have notated them for the most common meters: C, ₵, (2/4), (3/4 and 6/8). In addition, we have listed a great many variations from which the guitarist may choose, depending on his ability, taste, and mood. There are other strums listed which are for special situations, and are much less frequently used.

As an aid to those guitarists who are less expert, we have included diagrams for fingering those chords which are required to play the songs in this book. They are organized according to key.

Each song will suggest its own style of accompaniment. Remember that simplicity is inherent in folk music. Once the style is established, two things are most important:

1) Don't hesitate to make up your own strums.
2) Feel free to pick, strum, hammer or what have you when it comes to accompanying these songs. Enjoy yourself.

STRUM I

One of the two basic strums. The thumb strikes the appropriate bass note on the first beat. On the second beat, the first three fingers swing and pluck simultaneously strings 1, 2, 3. This pattern is repeated according to the meter of the song. The circled numbers represent the strings with string 1 the high E string. The open numbers represent the fingers, with finger 1 the forefinger.

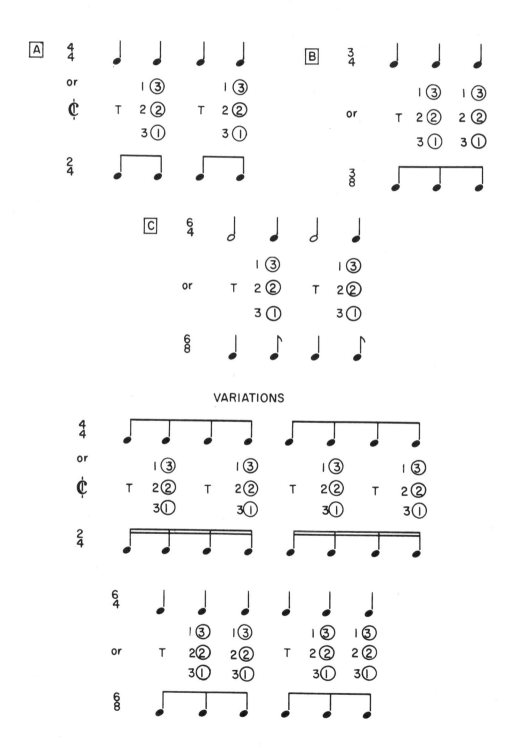

356

STRUM II

The second basic strum is similar to Strum I, except that the thumb strikes the bass note, then continues strumming across strings 1, 2, 3. For best results, strike the bass note with the thumbnail, and strum with the fleshy side of the thumb. Try to move only the thumb, not the hand or arm.

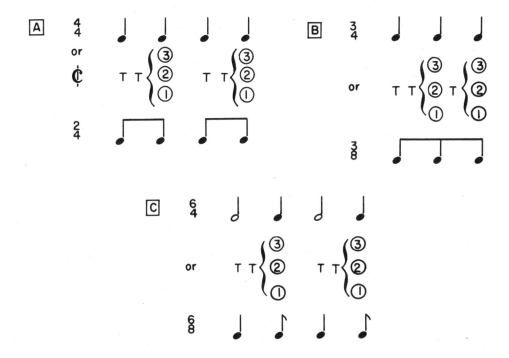

VARIATIONS

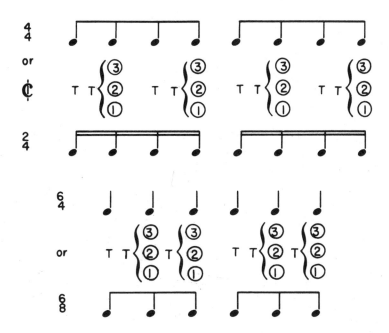

357

STRUM III

This is commonly called the Carter Family style, used by a folk singing group from the late Twenties into the Forties. Maybelle Carter continues to use this style today.

The thumb strikes the bass note on the first beat. On the second beat, finger 1 brushes down across strings 1, 2, 3, then finger 1 brushes up and strikes string 1: bump dit-ty, bump dit-ty.

The melody may sometimes be played by the thumb on the bass notes, while the rhythm is carried out by the brushing of the first finger. This strum can be used effectively with many songs from the South.

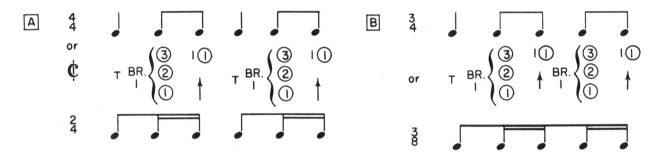

STRUM IV

This is a variation of Strum I. In (A) the thumb strikes the bass note on the first beat. The second beat is divided into two eighth notes; on note 1, finger 1 picks string 3, on note 2, fingers 2 and 3 pluck strings 2 and 1. Beat three is another bass note played by the thumb. On beat four, strings 3, 2, and 1 are plucked. (B) and (C) are metric variations of (A), just described.

358

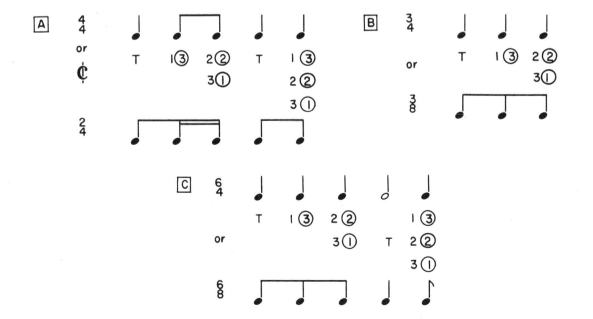

STRUM V

This beautiful arpeggio is useful in accompanying songs in slower tempos. In strum (A), the thumb strikes the bass note, finger 1 plucks string 3, then fingers 2 and 3 pluck strings 1 and 2 simultaneously, finishing with finger 1 replaying string 3. This must be varied in (B) and (C) to fit the various meters. A number of variations are listed.

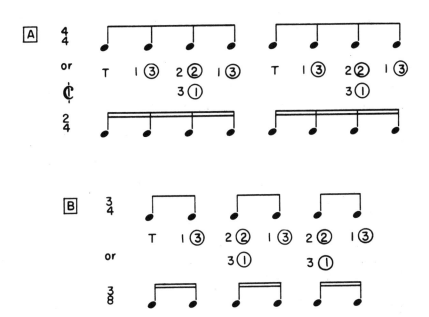

VARIATIONS

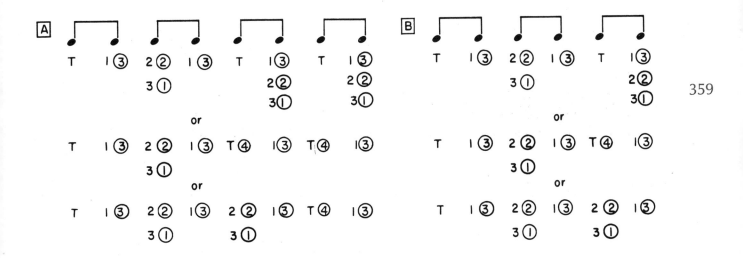

359

STRUM VI

This is one of the simplest arpeggios. In (A), the thumb plays the bass note, finger 1 plucks string 3, finger 2 plucks string 2, finger 3 plucks string 1; then finger 2 again plucks string 2, finger 1 plucks string 3, the thumb plays an alternate bass note, and finger 1 plucks string 3.

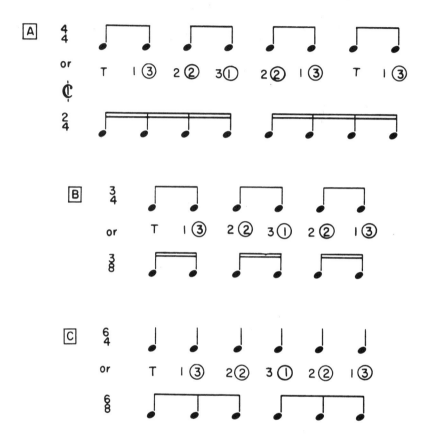

VARIATIONS

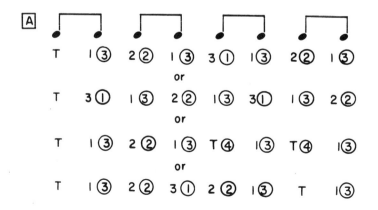

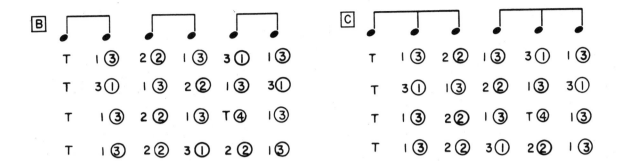

STRUM VII

Commonly called the Elizabeth Cotton style, the rhythm is carried on the *alternating* bass notes, and the melody or harmony is played on strings 1 and 2. The thumb strikes the bass note, finger 2 plucks string 2 (or 1, depending on the note desired). The thumb again plays an *alternate* bass note. (Do not repeat the bass note twice in a row.) Finger 1 then plucks string 3.

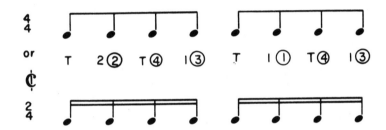

STRUM VIII

The thumb strikes a bass note, followed by finger brushing *up* across strings 3, 2, and 1. Then the thumb brushes *down* across strings 4, 3, 2, and 1, and finger 1 brushes *up* across strings 3, 2, and 1. The bass notes should alternate.

The tempo can be made more exciting by doubling the number of strums in each bar.

361

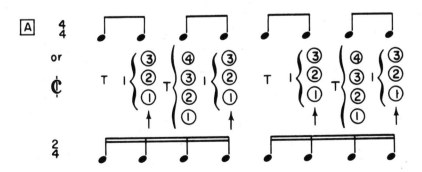

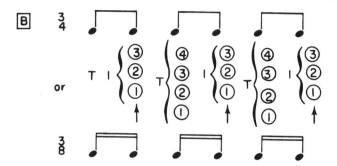

STRUM IX

This strum has two specific uses. For accompanying songs which are free and out of tempo, strum with the thumb across all the strings, following the chord changes. For accompanying strongly rhythmic, martial songs, follow the same procedure of strumming *down* with the thumb, but in the tempo of the song. The first use requires no example. The second use; play all.

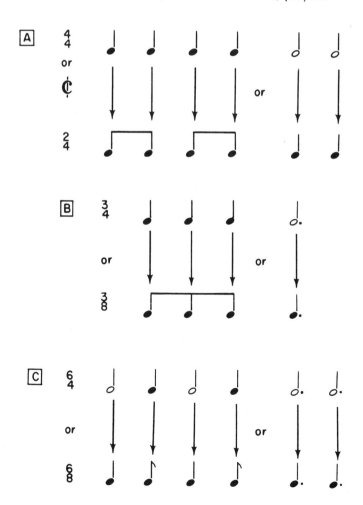

362

STRUM X

The thumb strikes a bass note, finger 1 plucks string 1; thumb plays an *alternate* bass note, then finger 1 plucks string 2. Thumb plays another bass note and then strums across strings 4, 3, 2, 1.

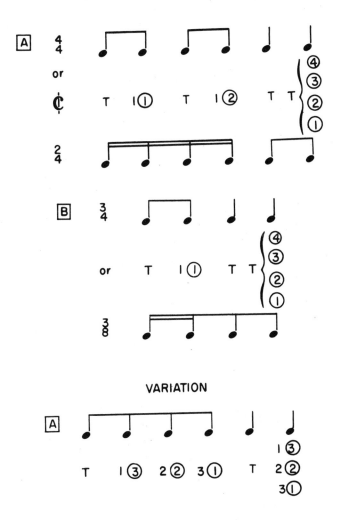

STRUM XI

The thumb plucks a bass note then strums across strings 4, 3, 2, 1; followed quickly by finger 1 brushing *up* across strings 1, 2, 3. Then the whole pattern is repeated. This is particularly useful for the "Blues."

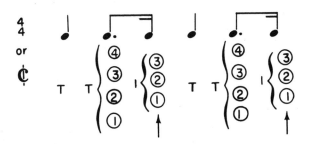

STRUM XII

This is a simple Latin-American strum. The thumb plucks a bass note, then strums *down* twice, omitting string 4 in the second strum. This is followed by thumb, strum, thumb strum, again omitting string 4 in the second strum.

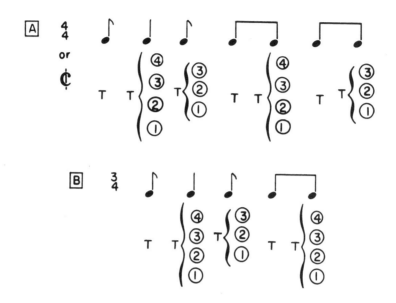

VARIATIONS

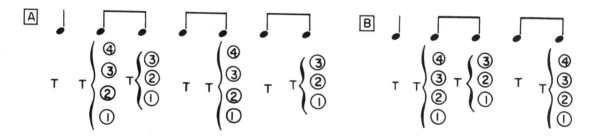

STRUM XIII

This is a metric variation of Strum I.

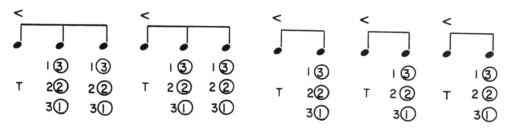

STRUM XIV

This is a strum used by Cisco Houston and Woody Guthrie. The thumb plucks a bass note, finger 3 plucks string 1, finger 2 plucks string 2, finger 1 plucks string 3. The third beat is an *alternate* bass note played by the thumb. On beat four, the first three fingers pluck strings 3, 2, 1 simultaneously.

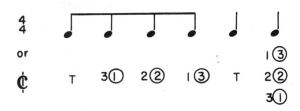

GUITAR CHORDS

Following are fingerings for the chords most frequently used in this book.
To avoid the problem of finding them out of context, they are listed in re-
lation to the keys in which they are most likely to be needed. This makes
for some repetition, but should make their use considerably easier.

KEY   CHORD CHART

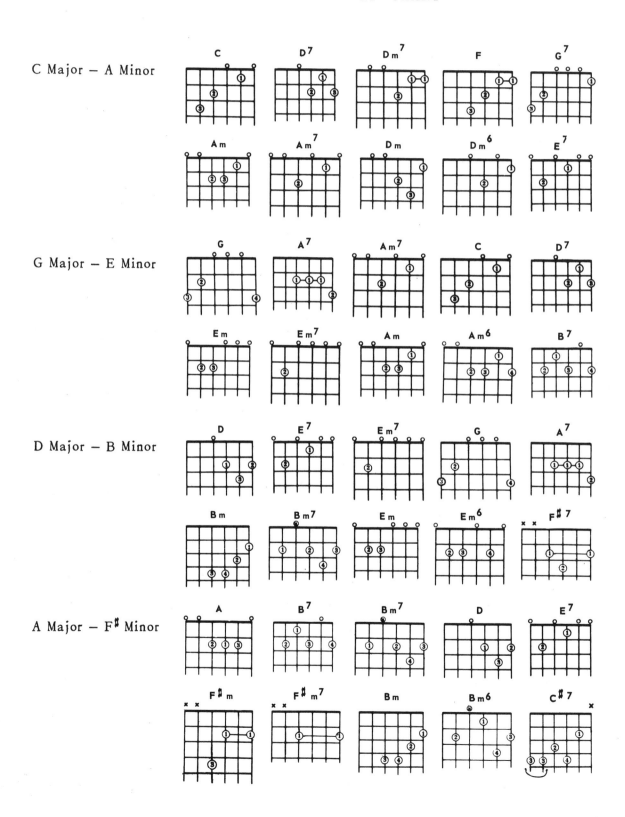

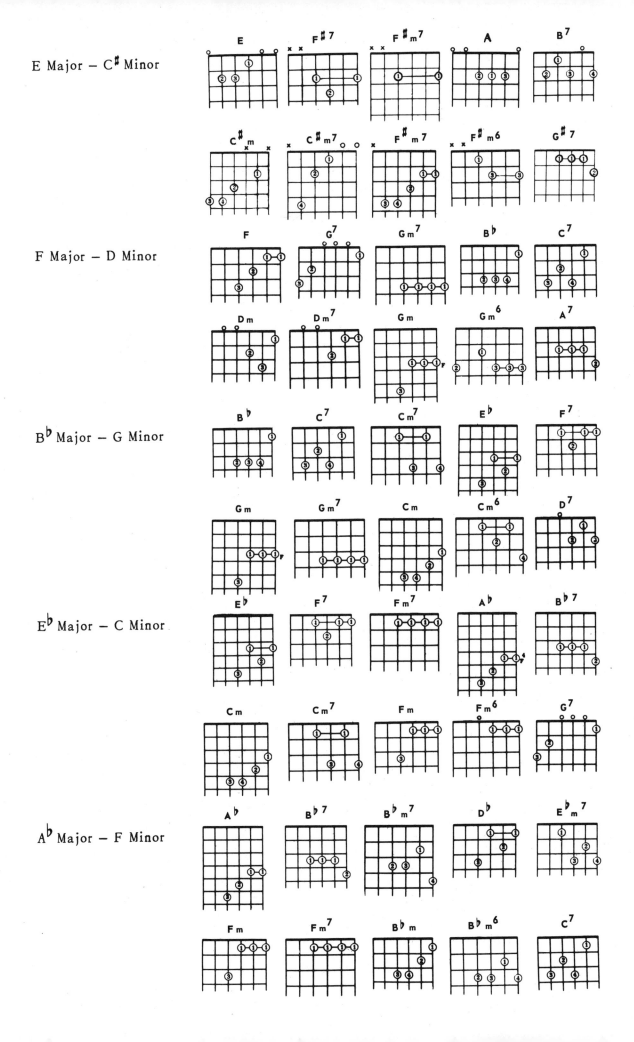

INDEX

368